TRI

'I never fall in love with nurses. They can be more dangerous than female patients.'

So Mark Barlow coolly informs Nurse Gillian Grant at their turbulent first encounter. But Gillian is in no danger of falling for the arrogant surgeon—or is she?

*Books you will enjoy
in our Doctor–Nurse series*

TRIO OF DOCTORS

BY

LINDSAY HICKS

MILLS & BOON LIMITED
London · Sydney · Toronto

First published in Great Britain 1983
by Mills & Boon Limited, 15–16 Brook's Mews,
London W1A 1DR

© Lindsay Hicks 1983

Australian copyright 1983
Philippine copyright 1983

ISBN 0 263 74408 6

Set in 10 on 12 pt Linotron Times
03/0983–54,000

Photoset by Rowland Phototypesetting Ltd
Bury St Edmunds, Suffolk
Made and printed in Great Britain by
Richard Clay (The Chaucer Press) Ltd
Bungay, Suffolk

CHAPTER ONE

GILLIAN was late for her first day's work at Greenvale. Nothing had gone right for her that morning, she thought, fuming behind the wheel of her little car while an articulated lorry slowly inched back and forth in a careful manoeuvre that held up the stream of traffic in both directions.

Her alarm clock had failed to go off and she had woken with a start at the sound of mail being thrust through the letter-box of her rented flat. She had snatched a cup of coffee and a piece of toast between showering and scrambling into the new and very elegant uniform of a Greenvale nurse. Her usually reliable Mini had refused to start for all her frantic efforts and she had been grateful to the dishy man in the neighbouring flat who had produced a set of jump leads and managed to get the car going.

Now she was stuck in a traffic jam with another two miles to drive to the clinic on the outskirts of the town. Privately owned and with an excellent reputation, Greenvale had impressed her when she went for an interview after applying for the advertised job. Being a Kit's nurse and proud of it, she had meant to impress Greenvale with her efficiency – and what a way to begin, she mourned with another frustrated glance at her watch. For punctuality was one of the first essentials for a nurse.

At last, the lorry driver achieved his aim of reversing

into a very narrow access and Gillian and everyone else was free to continue on their way. The little Mini shot forward impatiently. So did a sleek Mercedes, turning right and cutting across the traffic in the obvious hope of beating every other car off the mark. Gillian stood on the brake, heart in her mouth. She glared. With a casual wave of his hand, the driver of the Mercedes acknowledged her enforced halt and drove on at speed.

She was furious. She had caught only a glimpse of the man. But smooth good looks with a hint of arrogance convinced her that whoever or whatever he was, he didn't give a damn for anyone else on the road – or in the world, probably. Seething, she drove on.

She passed the Mercedes just before she got to Greenvale. For all the motorist's dangerous haste, he had stopped at a newsagent and he emerged with an armful of newspapers and magazines just as Gillian's Mini drew level with the shop door. It was the silver car that caught her eye, she wasn't interested in its driver. But, driving past, she did notice that he was very tall and immaculately dressed in a silver-grey suit. He was as smooth and as sleek as his expensive Mercedes, she thought scornfully, dismissing him.

The clinic was set back from the road, a large and graciously lovely mansion that had been extensively modernised and skilfully extended. It had thirty beds and the most up-to-date equipment, and called upon the skills of some very eminent specialists and surgeons who were happy to be associated with the well-run Greenvale.

Gillian drove around to the back of the house and the staff car park. Leaving her Mini in the first available space, she seized the bag that held her cap and clean aprons and dashed across the car park towards the staff entrance. As she did so, a silver-grey Mercedes drove in her direction and it was the driver's turn to brake sharply to avoid an accident. With her mind on the time and busily framing abject apologies and explanations, Gillian just hadn't seen or heard the approaching car—and he had obviously taken the corner much too fast anyway, she thought indignantly, as the brakes squealed.

Glowering, he opened the car window with a touch of a button. 'Why the devil don't you look where you're going, woman!' With his mind on other things, he hadn't seen her until it was almost too late.

Gillian's hackles rose and her chin flew up at his tone. 'I could say the same thing to you! You just carved me up in the High Street!'

He raised an eyebrow. 'Oh, was that you? Then that scruffy little Mini belongs to you, does it? I'd be grateful if you'd move it. You've parked it in a reserved space.'

'I'm damned if I will!' Very blue eyes that were almost violet and fringed by ridiculously long lashes sparked fire. 'I'm in a hurry. It stays where it is!' She turned and stalked towards the building, breast heaving. She didn't know when she had last met someone so insufferable, so full of his own importance, so instantly dislikeable.

Gillian heard the scrunch of tyres as he spun the Mercedes in search of somewhere else to park but she didn't look back.

She knew the type, she thought scornfully. During her years at Kit's, she had often come into contact with senior surgeons or consultants who regarded junior nurses as less than dust and a qualified nurse as little more than an efficient robot in cap and apron. She didn't doubt that he was a member of the medical fraternity or that he was professionally connected with Greenvale. She just hoped that their paths wouldn't cross too often.

She ran up the shallow stone steps, pushed through narrow swing doors and hurried along to the office to announce her belated arrival.

Miss Kenny was prepared to be gracious in view of the fact that it was Nurse Grant's first day but her manner implied that she had expected better from a Kit's nurse. Gillian bit her lip, apologised anew for the chapter of accidents that had made her late and followed the grey-haired administrator to the floor where she was to work.

Greenvale was run on the lines of a cottage hospital with four floors, each consisting of six comfortable rooms and a pleasant day lounge in the new wing, and six luxurious suites for wealthier patients in the main wing. There were two splendid operating theatres, an X-ray department and plaster room, a swimming pool and gymnasium for convalescent patients, pharmacy and pathology department and a research laboratory; and an impressive set of consulting rooms where visiting specialists examined their patients and decided on suitable treatment. There was also a resident team of highly-qualified doctors and nurses and technicians, and an efficient domestic staff.

Greenvale was the fulfilled dream of an industrial tycoon who had recognised the readiness of people to pay for surgery and post-operative care, for medical treatment for themselves and their families, and had set out to supply the best possible surroundings and attention. Some patients came a considerable distance, such was Greenvale's reputation and the impressive list of specialists associated with it.

Gillian learned that there was a ratio of two nurses to every patient. She wasn't likely to be overworked, she thought dryly, remembering Kit's and the chronic shortage of staff to cope with the never-ending routines and daily emergencies of a busy London hospital that took patients from every part of the country for specialist treatment and some of the finest nursing care in the world.

Life at Greenvale promised to be much more relaxed. Nurses obviously had time to be really involved with their work and with the patients. At the same time, they might not be so helpful towards fellow-nurses, Gillian thought shrewdly. At Kit's, she had often stretched herself to do a junior's work as well as her own when they were particularly busy, knowing that a colleague would do the same for her if necessary. The camaraderie of a busy teaching hospital probably didn't exist at Greenvale and she felt that might not be the only aspect of Kit's that she would miss.

However, the work would be much the same. Having nursed patients in the private wing at Kit's, she knew that they could be demanding and autocratic but just as full of fears and fancies as anyone else, needing sympathy and reassurance and real concern from the nurses who looked after them.

As she walked along the wide, rubber-floored corridor with Miss Kenny, Gillian listened and looked about her with interest as the older woman outlined the layout of the clinic and the hierarchy of the staff. Greenvale was so much smaller than Kit's that it would take only a day or two to know her way about, she felt, recalling weeks of confusion during the early days of her training. Kit's was a veritable maze of wings and corridors and departments, swarming with hundreds of staff and hordes of patients and visitors. It was obvious that she would soon know everyone at Greenvale—if only by sight and name.

A door opened on the sound of a man's deep and obviously irritated voice, and a moment later he came out into the corridor. Tall and lean with crisply curling dark hair and deep-set grey eyes, immaculately dressed in a grey suit, he was a handsome man but an angry scowl marred his rather sensual good looks. He emerged so abruptly that he almost collided with the two women. He checked his stride with a curt apology, not managing a smile.

'Good morning, Mr Barlow. Having problems?' Miss Kenny was unruffled by a familiar brusqueness.

'Nothing I can't handle.' He nodded, about to walk on, his glance sweeping indifferently over the slender girl in the pale green of a Greenvale nurse.

Observing that glance, Miss Kenny detained him with a brisk: 'Miss Grant is our new surgical nurse. She comes to us from St Christopher's and I know you'll agree that she couldn't have a better recommendation.' She turned to Gillian, smiling. 'Mr Barlow is our resident senior surgeon, Miss Grant. So you'll be working together very often.'

Gillian's heart sank. There was nothing she liked about the man even on a second meeting. She suspected that he would be impossible to work with, impatient, demanding, fault-finding at every turn and not at all impressed with her Kit's qualifications.

'We've already met,' he said impatiently, too busy for unnecessary introductions. 'Perhaps you would inform Miss Grant that she mustn't leave her car in my parking space in future.'

He strode away, leaving Gillian bristling and the administrator quite taken aback. 'I didn't realise that you knew each other . . .'

'We don't,' Gillian said firmly. 'We clashed over parking spaces a few minutes ago, that's all.'

'Oh, I see.' She sighed. 'It's something he does get cross about, I'm afraid—but you couldn't be blamed for not knowing about the parking arrangements, of course.' She hesitated. 'Mark Barlow is a really marvellous surgeon and we're very lucky to have him so we make rather more allowances than is probably good for him. He has a very quick temper and *he* doesn't make allowances at all.' She smiled wryly. 'You'll soon learn his little ways, I expect.'

Gillian smiled in polite response and said nothing, thinking a great deal as they walked on. She wasn't optimistic about her working relationship with the insufferable Mark Barlow. She didn't care how many allowances other people might make for him. She wasn't impressed by good looks or ability.

In her experience, the really able surgeons who were destined to make a name for themselves in their profession were the sweetest and gentlest and most modest of men. It was only those who had too high an opinion of themselves and their work who walked all over everyone and didn't give a damn if they hurt or offended anyone on their way to the top. Mark Barlow might regard himself as some kind of superior being. In her view, he was just a pig!

She was astonished to find that almost every other nurse at Greenvale considered him to be something special. She conceded that he was good-looking—if one liked the type. She supposed that he might be regarded as a very eligible bachelor—if one was prepared to put up with his chauvinistic attitudes for the sake of money and position. She realised with some scorn that his obvious lack of interest in mere nurses made him a highly desirable object of pursuit.

It seemed that every girl thought that *she* might be the one to win Mark Barlow's heart if only he could be persuaded to take some notice of her in the first place.

Gillian was almost amused. But it really wasn't funny that any girl should be prepared to swallow her pride and any amount of rebuffs for the sake of a man like Mark Barlow, she thought indignantly. Even on that very first day at Greenvale, when perhaps it wasn't fair to make snap judgments, she knew that they would clash again and again.

Perhaps there was too much likeness of temperament. For Gillian had a quick temper too. And she was proud, passionately so at times. She wasn't a conceited girl but she did know that she was a good nurse who quickly established a rapport with patients because she really cared that they should get well. She was fiercely independent and experience had taught her to be wary of men and reluctant to commit herself too soon to any relationship. Five years of nursing had matured an impulsive girl into a responsible and level-headed young woman who might dream of husband, home and children but certainly didn't mean to sacrifice her nursing career for any man at the drop of a hat.

As it happened, only one man had ever suggested marriage and she had turned him down. But there had been plenty of men who suggested everything but, she thought wryly. Kit's was full of young doctors and medical students who pursued pretty nurses with amorous intent but simply couldn't afford to fall seriously in love. Junior nurses soon learned not to take them seriously and light-hearted flirtation was regarded as one of the 'perks' of working in a busy teaching hospital.

Gillian had flirted, too. It had been a very necessary relaxation after long hours on the wards or too many evenings spent with text-books, worrying about exams. She had acquired lots of good friends but not one lover during her years at Kit's.

She wasn't a prude but she didn't care for the idea of casual sex. She felt that she would need to love a man very much before she went to bed with him and so far she hadn't met any man who could stir her heart to real and lasting love. Like any girl, she had known her heart to race and her senses to quicken at a smile or a kiss. She had been very fond of more than one man in her life. But she had been careful not to confuse affection and physical attraction with loving. She was quite sure that she would recognise the real thing if it ever came along and she didn't want to have any regrets about lost virginity if and when it happened. Perhaps it was old-fashioned but Gillian was keeping herself for the man she was destined to love. Not necessarily for marriage, she conceded, knowing the limitations of a sensual nature. But certainly for love . . .

She had been very happy at Kit's. But six months of intensive theatre work had been exhausting and her resistance to infection had become so low that a touch of 'flu had turned into a severe bout of pneumonia and a spell in intensive care. It had been Gillian's first experience of life on the other side of the thermometer. It had been a very valuable experience but one she was in no hurry to repeat!

Convalescent and idly glancing through the *Nursing Mirror*, she had seen the advertisement for a surgical nurse at the Greenvale Clinic. She had been advised against returning to demanding hospital work for the time being and a friend had suggested that she should try private nursing. An interview at the clinic had led to the offer of a year's contract—and here she was. Far from home and family and all her friends but determined to enjoy a new challenge, she told herself firmly—and she wouldn't allow Mark Barlow to be the fly in the ointment!

He was operating that morning and Gillian discovered that she had been assigned to one of his patients. Mrs Maddox was middle-aged, very fat, with a history of gynaecological trouble as well as a slight heart condition and high blood pressure. She had been admitted to Greenvale some days before for rest and diet and careful observation before a hysterectomy.

Gillian was preparing her for Theatre when Mark Barlow walked into the room without ceremony to make his own final check on the condition of his patient.

She had wondered if his bedside manner would be a redeeming feature—and discovered that it was totally lacking. He was courteous but there was no trace of practised charm or any concession at all to the fact that Mrs Maddox would be presented with a very large bill for his surgical services in due course.

He had all the arrogance of a man who knew his skill and sensitivity as a surgeon and had no patience with anyone who doubted it. Fortunately Mrs Maddox appeared to have a great deal of faith in him and didn't seem to mind the lack of warmth. Oddly enough, the cool impersonality of the man's attitude was very reassuring, Gillian thought, surprised. Perhaps it was that undoubted confidence in himself, so irritating to her, that made his patients feel that they were in the best possible hands.

In response to a brisk request, she passed the patient's chart to him. Their fingers touched slightly and he glanced at her as though he saw her for the first time since entering the room. Until that moment, she had merely been just another nurse, she realised, unsurprised. Grey eyes narrowed and seemed to harden. Gillian looked back at him coldly, with dislike.

He scanned the chart and she saw him frown. 'When was the blood pressure last checked?'

'A few moments ago. I've just entered it.' Gillian indicated her neat figures in the column.

'Then note the time, Nurse,' he said coldly. 'I'm not a mind-reader and it happens to be a very important detail.'

She was too well-trained to make any retort. But her breast swelled with indignation that he should address her as though she was the greenest of junior nurses. She suspected it was deliberately offensive but the slight on her efficiency wasn't likely to instil confidence in the patient, she thought angrily.

She swallowed her fury. 'I'm sorry. I was about to do so when you came in.' Flustered by his unexpected and unannounced entrance, she had returned the chart to its hook without completing her notes.

'Very well. Take more care in future, please. Make a note of the time before you enter the figures and then it won't be forgotten,' he suggested as though she was a very junior nurse. He turned to his patient. 'Nurse will give you an injection very shortly, Mrs Maddox. You'll feel relaxed after it and look forward to our theatre date instead of dreading it.'

She chuckled. 'Oh, I'm not anxious, Doctor. It will be a relief to be rid of the cause of all the trouble and Mrs Foster says that you left her with a very neat scar.'

'You'll still be able to wear a bikini,' he assured her carelessly.

'A bikini! You have to be joking!' she declared, deriding her own size with a jolly laugh. 'But it would be nice, I must say,' she added wistfully.

'It could happen if you'd only follow my advice and keep to a rigid diet – and it would solve a few more of your health problems,' he said briskly. 'You're carrying far too much weight for a woman of your age.'

As the door closed on him, Mrs Maddox leaned back on her pillows with a little sigh. 'He's a dream, isn't he? The strong, silent type—and so good-looking! Doesn't he make your heart turn over, Nurse Grant? I envy you with your looks and figure and all your chances, working with a man like Mark Barlow. He wouldn't even look at a suet pudding like me if it wasn't his job!'

Gillian looked at her, astonished. How could any self-respecting woman glow so foolishly after such off-hand treatment? He had been almost contemptuous. She knew that she'd have been tempted to slap his face if he'd spoken to her so—and she'd have done it too, she thought hotly, indignant on the woman's behalf as she seemed oblivious of any offence, intended or otherwise.

'I daresay you're all in love with him,' Mrs Maddox swept on teasingly. 'I did hear that he's running around with Louise Penistone again now that she's home. She's a lovely girl, isn't she? Very spoiled, of course . . . the apple of Hugh Penistone's eye. I expect he's ambitious.

Men usually are, aren't they? Mark Barlow wouldn't be the first man to marry the boss's daughter, in a manner of speaking.'

Gillian turned to the door. 'It's time for your pre-med, Mrs Maddox. I'll be back in a moment.' Out in the corridor, she paused for a moment to draw a deep breath. After only two hours in her new job, she had come into contact with a thoroughly detestable man that she wouldn't touch with a barge-pole—and discovered that every other woman in the vicinity seemed to think that he was a gift from the gods! Either there was something wrong with her antennae and she was getting all the wrong vibrations or everyone else at Greenvale was quite mad!

He was still on the ward, an unmistakable figure with that proud, dark head and the lean, muscular build. She supposed he *was* good-looking if one liked dark curls and steely grey eyes and strong, sensual features in a tanned face, she admitted grudgingly. He was talking to Penny Hughes, nurse in charge, and he actually appeared to be smiling, she observed dryly. It seemed that he could be human if and when he chose.

Suddenly he turned and came towards her, tall and lithe and very impressive. Seeing her, his expression visibly hardened. Gillian again felt that there was something quite ruthless about Mark Barlow. If she didn't promptly move out of his way, he would probably trample her underfoot rather than change direction, she thought bitterly.

She remained quite still, blocking his passageway. Nearing, he raised an eyebrow but didn't check his stride. He was due in Theatre and he didn't have time to be amused by her obvious militancy. Having clashed headlong at their first encounter, she was not prepared to like him, he knew. Well, he hadn't found anything to like in her so far – and he wasn't too inclined to look further.

Gillian's chin tilted. 'Mr Barlow! May I have a word?' It was an unmistakable challenge.

Mark was forced to stop. He looked his reluctance, glancing pointedly at his wrist-watch. 'Well? What is it?'

'When you have occasion to rebuke me for an over-sight kindly don't do so in front of the patient!' she snapped, eyes sparkling. 'I'm not used to that kind of thing. At St Christopher's, senior surgeons are usually the most courteous of men!'

'Don't be a fool, woman,' he said curtly, attempting to pass. 'If you make a mistake with any of my patients you may certainly expect to hear about it!'

She caught at his arm. 'We're going to have to work together, like it or not!' she fumed. 'Don't let's make it quite impossible for each other!'

He looked down at her, a glimmer of mockery in the deep-set grey eyes. 'I must say it's an original approach,' he drawled. 'But you're wasting your time—and all that passion. You're a pretty girl and I expect they went down like ninepins at Kit's when you flashed those bright eyes. But anyone will tell you that I never get involved with nurses. They can be more dangerous than female patients in my experience.' Coolly, he detached her hand from his arm and walked away.

Gillian's usually ready tongue was silenced by sheer shock—and temper. The arrogance—the conceit—the bloody nerve of the man! To suppose that she could be interested in him. To imply that she was trying to attract his notice with a pretence of hostility. To be so blind to her very real dislike and contempt. To dismiss her as a mere nothing!

She had never been so angry in her life—she had never been so insulted in her life. Certainly she had never been so lost for words . . .

CHAPTER TWO

NURSE first and foremost, Gillian managed to choke back her fury and hurried along the corridor to the clinical room where the drugs were kept in a locked cupboard. Mrs Maddox was due for her pre-med and if her arrival in Theatre was delayed through any fault of hers, she didn't doubt that Mark Barlow would delight in pointing it out as offensively as possible.

Penny Hughes was checking stock in the clinical room. She just nodded when Gillian asked if she would check the dosage for the pre-med injection and ticked another item off on her list.

Laying up a tray to give the injection, Gillian sensed a slight reserve in the other nurse's manner and knew that she had observed that encounter between herself and Mark Barlow and had wondered, too distant to overhear anything that was said but certainly aware that it wasn't friendly.

Penny seemed to be steeling herself to comment. Gillian waited, her slender hands busy with a hypodermic syringe and an ampoule.

'Have you known Mark Barlow long?'

It was an apparently idle question, put much too casually. A flicker of amusement touched Gillian's eyes. 'Long enough,' she returned, just as casually, seeing no reason to satisfy the other girl's obvious curiosity. Long enough to know that she didn't want to know him any better, she thought with feeling.

'I didn't know that you were a local girl?'

Gillian smiled. 'I'm not. London born and bred, as a matter of fact,' she said lightly.

Penny glanced at the silver badge of the state registered nurse that Gillian wore so proudly on the bib of her apron. Her expression cleared as if she had solved a mystery. 'I see you trained at St Christopher's. I suppose that's where you met Mark?'

Gillian was carefully checking the level in the syringe. 'No,' she said absently and with truth, rather surprised that there should be any connection between Mark Barlow and Kit's. Penny's words seemed to imply that he had qualified at the famous hospital in London. It was perfectly possible, of course. But it must have been before she began her training. He was the kind of man who wouldn't be easily forgotten, she thought dryly.

She handed the hypodermic to Penny for checking. Then, smiling her thanks, she hurried away to administer the injection to the waiting Mrs Maddox. She felt almost sorry for Penny who had obviously been aching to know all about her relationship with the surgeon. Some relationship! But she supposed it was misleading that they should have been slanging each other like old enemies when they were utter strangers.

In a way, their clashes had established an awareness of each other that might never have happened during an entire year at Greenvale, she realised with a slight shock of surprise. Dislike at first sight could be emotionally involving, after all. For she wasn't likely to forget her first day in the new job or her first encounter with Mark Barlow.

Later, she accompanied Mrs Maddox to the theatre

floor. The big woman was drowsy, rather euphoric and quite untroubled by any doubts or fears as the trolley was trundled along the corridor and into the lift by a porter, Gillian leading the way.

It was her first glimpse of Theatre with its ante-rooms and recovery rooms and gleaming array of modern equipment. She was impressed. But it was surgical skill that really mattered and Mark Barlow was still an unknown quantity as far as she was concerned.

She had watched the masters in action, after all. He might have all the right qualifications but he couldn't compare with Sir Geoffrey Butler, Professor of Surgery, or with Paul Ritchie or Hamilton Mann, pioneers in their respective fields and famous for their advanced and courageous techniques.

She would have liked to watch Mark Barlow at work, however. In fact, she would have liked to assist that morning. Gillian enjoyed theatre work and knew she was good at it, she had worked with some of the most able and demanding of surgeons during her months as a theatre sister at Kit's. She was hoping to work in the theatre at Greenvale even if it would bring her into rather closer contact with Mark Barlow than she would wish.

Steve Palmer, the anaesthetist, was waiting in an ante-room for the patient. He greeted Mrs Maddox with a few words of cheerful reassurance, hypodermic needle at the ready. Within seconds of the injection in her hand, she was fast asleep and breathing stertorously.

Steve borrowed a few moments out of his busy morning to appraise the pretty face and slender figure and shining hair of the hovering nurse. He grinned at her suddenly. 'I haven't seen *you* before,' he said with a warmth of admiration. 'You must be our new surgical nurse.'

She liked his pleasant smile, his easy and acceptable friendliness. 'Gillian Grant,' she volunteered readily, smiling.

'Welcome to Greenvale, Gillian. When I'm not so busy I'll give you a warmer welcome,' he promised, eyes twinkling. 'In fact, I'll buy you a drink one evening if the boyfriend doesn't object.'

Her eyes danced. 'I'd like that—and there isn't a boyfriend,' she said lightly, obligingly.

The swing doors of the prepared theatre swung back and a tall, green-gowned figure, complete with boots, mask and surgical gloves, appeared in the doorway.

'I'm waiting for my patient,' he announced brusquely. 'She'll be coming round if you don't get her in here and properly under, man!'

'Right!' Seeming not to mind the impatient tone of his colleague, Steve adjusted his own mask and trundled the trolley towards the open door.

Mark stepped to one side. Steely grey eyes regarded Gillian coldly above the green operating mask. Nothing was said but she bridled at the slight scorn in his manner which seemed to imply that he suspected her of delaying the anaesthetist with quite unnecessary flirtation. He must think she was man-mad, she thought crossly. For a brief moment, their eyes met and held, open hostility between them. Then he turned away and the swing doors closed on him.

Gillian discovered that her hands were tightly clenched. She smiled wryly at the evidence of tension. She was a fool to let him get under her skin so rapidly. But there was something about him that made all her hackles rise in a moment. But it wasn't an unreasonable dislike, she told herself firmly. He had given her plenty of reason to dislike him in a very short time.

She went to the door of the theatre and looked through the small round window with a very natural interest. Mrs Maddox was already on the operating table and Steve was busy with his complicated equipment. The theatre nurse was hovering over the trolley with its neat array of gleaming instruments. Mark Barlow stood slightly apart from the main tableau, very still, gloved hands poised for action and a scalpel at the ready. Gillian wondered if he was 'tuning in'.

She had known many surgeons and each one had their individual approach to their work. For instance, Peter Lincoln whistled under his breath and out of tune all the time he was operating, almost driving the theatre staff round the bend. Sir Geoffrey was very cheerful and loud-voiced, telling the most frightful jokes and talking non-stop as though his conversation was far more important than the patient on the operating table. He worked non-stop, too. Gillian had needed to be constantly alert so that each instrument was slapped into his hand at the very instant it was required.

Paul Ritchie was much slower, deliberate in his movements, explaining every step of an operation even to those who knew it by heart anyway. He was a brilliant surgeon but he had some irritating mannerisms. Philip Arne was good but somehow he didn't inspire confidence and theatre staff were usually on edge during his list, waiting tensely for something to go wrong— although it had never happened to Gillian's knowledge. Everyone breathed sighs of relief when he stepped back from the table and stripped off his gloves and mask.

Gillian lingered, watching intently as Mark Barlow stepped forward at a nod from the anaesthetist and prepared to cut down. His hands moved swiftly and deftly. She could almost sense the coolness and the confidence that emanated from the surgeon. It was impossible to imagine that his hand could falter or to suppose that there was the slightest doubt in his mind as to his skill or the swift recovery of the patient. She might not like him but she couldn't help admiring his professionalism.

She only wished that she was assisting instead of wistfully watching from a distance. She couldn't see exactly what he was doing but in her mind she followed every move and played the part of theatre nurse, handing him the right instrument at exactly the right moment and being quite indispensable.

Steve was the most important man in that theatre, of course. But somehow the anaesthetist's part in the drama was always overlooked. He sat at the patient's head, quietly adjusting taps and dials and carefully observing her condition and everyone forgot that her life was really in his hands for much of the time. Everyone except the surgeon who turned to him constantly for reassurance that all was well.

It was a straightforward hysterectomy and didn't take very long. Mark straightened after tying the last suture and stepped back, nodding satisfaction. Pulling down his mask, he turned to look directly at the eager face that was framed in the window.

It was just as if he had known all the time that she was watching, Gillian felt, disconcerted. And perhaps he had. For a surgeon had to be sensitive in many ways, after all.

She backed hastily away from the small but revealing window. She had just reached the outer door of the ante-room when he spoke.

'If you were interested, why didn't you scrub up and watch at close quarters?'

Gillian turned. 'I thought you might not appreciate an audience.'

He surveyed her thoughtfully. 'Interested in theatre work, are you? You won't learn about it from a distance.' His tone was dry.

Her chin went up. 'You seem to think that I'm a novice. I'm not only state registered but I've just had six months as a theatre sister at Kit's.'

Amusement glinted in the grey eyes. 'Well done,' he drawled.

Gillian glared, resenting the mockery in his tone. 'I'm a very good theatre nurse!'

He raised an eyebrow. 'Self-praise is no recommendation. You'll have to prove that to my satisfaction.'

'I've worked with some of the best surgeons in the country,' she told him indignantly.

'With plenty of back-up,' he pointed out. 'Surgical officers and housemen and other qualified nurses—and more on call if you need them. Here, it will be just you—and me! Heaven help you if I get the wrong instrument slapped in my hand at a crucial moment or if you fail to note something that I've overlooked.'

Gillian smiled scornfully. 'Is it possible that you could overlook anything?' she asked sweetly, very cutting.

'No.' Tone and manner were uncompromising. 'But you'll need to be constantly on your toes, anyway. I don't tolerate fools or incompetents—in or out of the theatre!'

Gillian boiled over. 'You really are a pig, aren't you?' she snapped.

He looked at her steadily. 'You don't have to like me. Just do your work properly, that's all. Personal feelings have no place in the operating theatre.'

'I shouldn't think they play *any* part in your life!'

'Very little,' he agreed smoothly.

Gillian glowered.

Steve put his head round the door of the ante-room. 'The patient's gone into recovery and doing nicely,' he announced. 'It's the ovarian cyst next, isn't it?' He winked at Gillian. 'Still with us? You didn't need to wait around for Mrs Maddox, you know. She'll be kept in the recovery room for an hour or so before going back to the ward.'

'I do know the routine,' she said tartly.

He blinked, taken aback by the snap in her voice. 'Sorry I spoke!'

Gillian smiled at him, contrite. He was really rather nice. Any man would seem nice after her brush with the infuriating and detestable Mark Barlow, of course, she admitted. But the cheerful anaesthetist was very easy to like and promised to be a friend. Newcomer to job and surroundings, she was going to be grateful for friends, after all.

'Sorry I snapped. But everyone's treating me like a very green junior,' she said with a bitter glance for the tall surgeon who stood with his arms folded and a sardonic expression on his good-looking face. 'I've been nursing for five years!'

Steve leaned over to look at her badge. 'Kit's nurse,' he said, impressed. 'We don't get many of those in our little backwater, do we Mark? You're a Kit's man, aren't you? Know each other?' He grinned at Gillian. 'I hope he isn't the lure that brings you to Greenvale, Gillian,' he went on, a mischievous twinkle in his blue eyes. 'I'd written you down as mine!'

'I never met him until today,' she said firmly, her tone unmistakably announcing that their meeting had not enriched her life in the least. Their eyes met across the small room. Chin tilting, she refused to recognise the gleam of amusement in the depths of the grey eyes that seemed incapable of smiling without mockery.

'She doesn't like you, Mark,' Steve declared, triumphant. 'I guess I've won the girl this time!'

Mark shrugged, moving to the door. 'I wasn't competing,' he said dryly. 'I don't share your absurd weakness for pretty nurses.' The door closed behind him.

Gillian looked after him with dislike. She turned to the anaesthetist. 'Are you friends?' she asked impulsively.

Steve laughed. 'Sure! Why not? He doesn't steal my women and he doesn't beat me at golf.'

She smiled doubtfully. 'Is that your criteria for friendship?'

'Can you think of a better one?' His tone was blithe. 'Women and golf are my main interests in life.'

She shook her head at him in amused reproach. 'I must go,' she said, rather reluctantly. 'Nurse Hughes will be wondering what's happened to me. I ought not to have stayed so long but surgery fascinates me, I must admit.'

'I saw the face at the window,' Steve told her, smiling. 'Why didn't you scrub up and come in? Mark wouldn't have noticed—or cared. Nothing disturbs his concentration when he's operating.'

'He's good, isn't he?' She had no real desire to praise the man but fair was fair. Even at a distance with the door between them and unable to see just what those strong, capable hands were doing, Gillian had been aware of his skill and sensitivity and the reassuring lack of tension in the theatre. Confident and relaxed, he had known just what to do and done it to the very best of his ability.

'Very good.' The assurance was firm, unhesitating.

She would enjoy working with a good surgeon, Gillian felt. She might even be able to overlook his unattractiveness as a person . . .

She went back to her ward and discovered that she hadn't been missed. She had been assigned to Mrs Maddox until her eventual discharge and it had been assumed that she would stay to watch the hysterectomy and await any special instructions from the surgeon.

Penny Hughes suggested that she went to lunch while Mrs Maddox was still in the recovery room. It had been an easy but eventful morning and Gillian emerged into the bright sunshine of the June day with a feeling of relief.

Taking her Mini, she drove a mile or so down the country road to a quaint little pub. She sat in its quiet garden with a glass of ice-cold lager and a sandwich. Two old men, half-asleep, were the only other occupants. Gillian looked about her with pleasure. It was warm and peaceful and very pleasant. Greenvale and Mark Barlow seemed a million miles away.

She wasn't sure how she felt about the new job. Greenvale was so different from Kit's and she had always liked to be busy, always responded to the challenge of each day in a big teaching hospital. She felt that there might be too much time on her hands, too little use made of her excellent training. But she had overdone things in those last weeks at Kit's before her illness. Perhaps she needed the calm, the slow pace of the backwater that was Greenvale, she thought, remembering the cheerful anaesthetist's description with a flicker of amusement.

She liked Steve. He was a type that she had met very often at Kit's—extrovert, cheerful and undemanding. They made good friends and obliging companions and didn't insist on being lovers. No doubt he would make a pass if she went out with him. They all did. But he would probably accept her lack of interest in casual sex with a philosophical shrug and a smile and be quite happy to go on seeing her on a friendly basis. Gillian didn't want any emotional complications while she was at Greenvale. So far, things were going well.

She had been lucky to find a ground-floor flat in an old house in the heart of the bustling market town. It was not only furnished but she had access to the small garden, little more than a patch of lawn and some scrubby flower-beds, but useful. She had leased the flat for a year at a remarkably reasonable rent. The furniture was shabby but comfortable, and somehow the place felt like home.

It was five years since Gillian had left the bosom of her family to train at Kit's. Then she had shared a cramped flat on the top floor of the Nurses' Home with three other first-years. Unusually, they had all completed their training and still been together five years later, state registered and working at Kit's, sharing a tiny terraced house in a side street conveniently near the hospital.

It was going to feel strange and perhaps rather lonely

at first, living alone. But Gillian was a very private person and there had been times when she had longed to get away from her friends, dear though they were. She could never have hurt their feelings by saying so. Now, Sue and Helen and Babsi were a hundred miles away and someone else had moved into the tiny box-room that had been her bedroom. So far, she had no regrets.

She liked the flat. She liked the small town and its friendly people. She liked the nearness to the sea, too, only twenty minutes' drive along the quiet roads and over the rolling Sussex downs.

Gillian loved the sea. She liked to stroll on the shore, feeling that every little anxiety, every uncertainty about the future, every irritation vanished before the soothing influence of wind and wave sweeping in from the sea.

Despite Mark Barlow's hostility and her own instinctive reaction to it, Gillian felt that she was going to enjoy her year at Greenvale. It would certainly be a new experience.

Relaxed and almost drowsy in the warm sun, watching a few birds fighting over the last crumbs of her sandwich, Gillian was more content than she had been for some time. Much as she loved nursing, happy as she had been at Kit's with her work and her friends and a full social life, there had always been a void that it seemed only one person could fill—and so far she hadn't found him. Perhaps she would prove to be mistaken but she had a feeling that she was destined to find her real happiness through this new job and new surroundings.

She had yet to meet the man who was her destiny, she felt. But he could be waiting around the very next corner . . .

A woman's light, carrying voice and a man's deep

drawl in response shattered the serenity of the afternoon. Gillian glanced towards the pub as Mark Barlow emerged into the sunshine, drinks in hand, following a girl who made her way towards some chairs set in the shade.

He must have removed that ovarian cyst in record time, Gillian thought, surprised to see him. But a glance at her watch showed that it was almost an hour since she had left Greenvale and his fast car could cover the short distance to the pub in moments.

It was time for her to go back to work but she was reluctant to abandon the quiet garden and the lovely day. No doubt he was free for the rest of the afternoon. Free to dance attendance on the girl in the floral silk dress who looked as though male admiration and attention were nothing new to her.

She was very lovely, Gillian admitted fairly. Jet black curls, expertly cut, made her own ash-blonde fairness seem insipid. Limpid brown eyes smiled on Mark Barlow with encouraging warmth. She had a classic beauty in face and figure, and a golden tan that she could not have acquired in England during an uncertain summer.

The surgeon was very attentive. Gillian was intrigued. For his brusque manner and arrogant attitude had made her wonder if he liked women at all. He obviously liked this one. Observing them, Gillian discovered that he had a smile that was particularly warm and attractive when he was setting out to charm rather than to alienate.

The girl was very confident. Her manner was proprietorial, just a little autocratic. Gillian was amused. It was unexpected that a man like Mark Barlow should so tamely come to heel for any woman, even such a beautiful one.

Louise Penistone.

The name leaped at her out of the blue. She couldn't possibly overhear their conversation from the far end of the garden. Yet she seemed to know the girl's name. She wrinkled her forehead, puzzled.

Mrs Maddox, she recalled suddenly. Talking about the surgeon and Hugh Penistone's daughter. She knew that Hugh Penistone was the businessman who had founded Greenvale—very wealthy, very successful. If that lovely girl really was his daughter then obviously she would know Mark Barlow just as well as her manner seemed to imply.

Was he ambitious? *Did* he plan to marry the boss's daughter, in a manner of speaking? With or without love? She wouldn't put it past him; Gillian thought dryly. He had struck her as being particularly cold-blooded for all the sensuality of those striking good looks. She had felt that he was ruthless without knowing anything at all about him. He would certainly have an eye to the main chance, she decided with a flicker of contempt.

He didn't see her as she crossed the garden on her way to her parked Mini. He only had eyes for the lovely, laughing girl at his side. Gillian was relieved. She might have to work with him but she didn't want even the smallest of social contacts with the man.

CHAPTER THREE

GILLIAN dismissed Mark Barlow and his girlfriend as she drove back to Greenvale. She was very tempted to park her Mini in its former place but it would be a hollow victory if he had no intention of returning to the clinic that afternoon.

Mrs Maddox had been returned to her own room. She was sleepy and confused after a morphine injection to relieve post-operative discomfort and unaware that the operation was over. She thought that she was still in the ante-room.

Gillian's afternoon was spent in routine observations of the patient's condition, regular checks of the saline drip and drainage tubes and in ensuring that Mrs Maddox was comfortable. Because of her heart condition, she was wired up to a monitor and the 'bleep' of the machine provided a steady and reassuring accompaniment to her work.

Another nurse arrived punctually to take over when Gillian was due to go off duty. Making a mental vow not to be late the next morning, come what may, she took off cap and apron in the locker room and admitted to feeling tired. She looked at herself in the wall mirror and saw that she was pale and that there were faint smudges of weariness beneath her eyes. She thought with longing of a hot bath, a lazy evening and an early night. It was her first day of nursing since she had been ill, she reminded herself. And she had spent a few hectic days moving into the flat and getting acquainted with her new surroundings.

She was unlocking the Mini when she heard her name, confidently called. She turned to see the auburn-haired anaesthetist approaching, very sure that she would be pleased to see him. Dressed in casual clothes, his hair rumpled where he had pulled an Aran sweater over his head, there was a warm smile in his blue eyes. He was attractive, reassuring.

Gillian smiled at him, wondering why she didn't resent that assured approach. Perhaps because it was accompanied by a genuine friendliness and a pleasing warmth of personality, she decided.

'Just going home?' he asked in his easy way.

She nodded. 'End of first day,' she said lightly.

'How did it go?'

'Very well, actually. Better than I really expected. Everyone is so . . . relaxed.'

His eyes twinkled. 'You're used to working under pressure, Gillian. Don't be misled by our easy-going attitude. We're a highly efficient team and we can match Kit's or any other general hospital for results any day of the week.'

'I don't doubt it . . .'

'Yes, you do. But I'll let you off as you're a very new girl. And a pretty one,' he added, his smile deepening.

Gillian dropped a mock curtsey. 'Thank you, sir, you're very kind.' She opened the car door and leaned over to put her bag on the passenger seat, a gentle hint that she didn't have the time or the inclination to stand about in the car park making idle conversation, no matter how nice or how friendly he seemed. 'I suppose

you're on your way home, too,' she added in a further
hint.

'This *is* home, love.' He took in the entire Greenvale
complex with an expansive wave of his hand. 'I'm a
resident anaesthetist and that means just what it says.
I've a couple of rooms in the staff annexe. Theoretically
I'm on call twenty-four hours a day. In actual fact, there
are two of us and we cover for each other. We don't have
too many emergencies and the job doesn't interfere too
much with my golf—or my love life.' He smiled at her
suddenly. 'Jeff is covering for me this evening. Why
don't we have that drink?'

She hesitated. 'Could we make it another time?'

'Sure—whenever you like.' He spoke lightly but there
was the hint of disappointment, the beginning of reserve.

'It isn't a brush-off,' Gillian told him with her usual
frankness. 'It's just that I'm dead on my feet.'

He looked down at her steadily. She had the almost
translucent skin of the true blonde but he observed the
pallor of weariness. The sparkle that he had so admired
in the vivid blue eyes had faded. She was a slight girl,
neat-waisted and slim-hipped with small, tilting breasts.
The pale green of the Greenvale uniform suited her
ash-blonde colouring and its expert tailoring emphasised
the attractive lines of her slender figure. She was a pretty
girl. She was a nice girl, too. Steve knew that he liked her
and wanted to know her better. He hoped that they were
going to be friends. He felt a slightly protective concern
for the girl with the sweet face and fragile appearance
and the apparent lack of stamina that was so surprising
for a Kit's nurse.

'Too much excitement for one day,' he said easily.

'Coming to Greenvale, meeting me . . .' His eyes twinkled. 'I prescribe a quiet evening with your feet up in front of the telly and a meal on a tray. How about a Chinese? There's a very good take-away in Market Street. I'll buy the food if you'll supply the plates. I am house-trained, by the way—and I come with excellent references,' he added reassuringly as Gillian sent him a swift, doubtful glance.

Gillian wasn't sure that she wanted to become so involved so soon. But he was very easy to like. She yielded, laughing. 'I suppose you know where I live?'

'Mary Kenny told me you'd taken a flat in Church Row,' he agreed simply.

'Number eighteen, ground floor.' Gillian got into the car, switched on the ignition. 'Seven o'clock suit?'

'Fine . . .' Steve looked after the little car, smiling.

Gillian drove through the narrow streets that were congested with the evening traffic and thought about the good-looking Steve Palmer and his eager interest. She wondered if it had been wise to be so encouraging. But a girl had to trust to her instincts and he had felt like a friend from their first moment of meeting. She needed all the friends she could find now that she was so far from Kit's and everyone she knew and loved.

Steve seemed harmless. She felt she could trust him. In any case, she was not a naive teenager without experience in handling amorous young men, she thought dryly—and she mustn't fall into the trap of supposing that every man had only one thing in mind. She knew that men regarded her as attractive, sexually desirable. Five years of warding off amorous young doctors and medical students had hammered that home. She firmly believed that any relationship depended on the girl's attitude to it. It shouldn't be necessary to go to bed with a man to hold him—and if it was, then he just wasn't worth bothering about!

If she made it quite clear at the outset that she wasn't interested in anything but friendship then she shouldn't have any problems with Steve, she decided confidently. He was very nice and probably dependable and she liked his light-hearted attitude to life. No doubt he had plenty of girlfriends, none of them very serious. Through Steve she would meet lots of other people, and wasn't that just what she needed?

It was good to turn the key in the lock and enter the welcoming flat. The sun slanted through windows that she had washed with eager enthusiasm when she moved in. Her books and records and pictures, and a few treasured pieces of porcelain turned it into home.

There were letters on the mat. One from home, one from Babsi. Gillian glanced through them and then tucked them into a drawer to savour at a more leisurely moment. Going into the bedroom, she unbuttoned the soft green frock with its darker collar and cuffs and put it away in the wardrobe. She kicked off the flat-heeled brogues that were easy on the feet but didn't do much for a girl's legs. Then she put on her dressing-gown and went to make tea while she waited for the slow-running hot tap to fill the bath.

She drank her tea and nibbled a biscuit to stave off the hunger pangs until Steve should arrive with the promised meal. She realised that she hadn't eaten enough that day. That was a mistake. It wasn't surprising that she felt so tired—almost drained. Home Sister at Kit's had always drummed into the juniors that it was very important for a nurse to eat well and regularly. Nursing was hard work and being rushed off one's feet ensured that one didn't put on any inches for all the stodginess of the meals served in the nurses' dining-room.

Putting on weight had never been a problem for Gillian. She felt that she was inclined to be too thin. Slender, small-boned, fair-haired and fair-skinned, she realised that she looked delicate and knew that her seniors in the past had often doubted her ability to cope with the demands of nursing. But looks were deceptive in her case. While other girls had gone down with colds and 'flu and other infections, Gillian had seemed to have a natural immunity to germs. In five years she had never spent a day in sick bay. So perhaps she had been ripe for that severe bout of pneumonia, she thought wryly. Certainly she wasn't as strong as she had been, although she had been passed as perfectly fit to return to work. ·

Fortunately, Greenvale wasn't going to be very demanding . . .

Steve was on time, announcing his arrival with a rhythmic punctuation of the bell that took her to the door with a smile in her eyes.

He smiled too. She was wearing a black silk kimono decorated with vivid flowers. Her pale, pretty hair was knotted at the back of her head and secured with a spray of artificial flowers. 'I like it,' he said warmly, in greeting.

Gillian laughed. 'I know it isn't Chinese but it's as near as I could get. It is Oriental, anyway. A friend brought it from Japan.'

'This friend has brought the food from China—or as near as I could get to it,' he told her lightly, presenting her with the cartons from the take-away restaurant.

'And some *sake*.' He produced a bottle of wine from behind his back.

Gillian looked at it doubtfully. 'That's very potent stuff, isn't it?'

'Only if you drink more than two thimblefulls, I'm told,' he said, straight-faced.

They laughed together.

'I'll see if I can find some thimbles,' she promised, heading for the kitchen.

Steve looked about him with interest. He walked across to read the titles of her books, and glance through the pile of records, to examine one or two of her ornaments.

'Nice place,' he commented as she came back into the room.

'I think so,' she agreed lightly. 'I was very lucky to find it. Did you see my garden?' she added with pride.

He walked to the window, looked out. '"*A garden is a lovesome thing, God wot*",' he quoted, amused. 'Until the grass wants cutting!'

'It does, doesn't it? There's a rusty old mower by the back door but I'm afraid it might fall to bits if I touch it.'

'I'm getting the message. Loud and clear,' he said, grinning. 'No wonder you invited me for supper.'

Eyes dancing, Gillian wrinkled her nose at him. 'You invited yourself for supper and must take the consequences!'

Steve gave a mock groan. 'Do I mow the lawn before or after we eat?'

'Oh, I couldn't impose on you like that . . .' she began.

'Yes, you could,' he said glumly.

She chuckled. 'Yes, I could,' she agreed blithely. '*After* we've eaten, don't you think . . . ?'

They were as easy with each other as old friends, she thought happily, liking him. Meeting someone like Steve on her very first day at Greenvale was an unexpected bonus—and it certainly made up for having to work with someone like Mark Barlow.

The food was good, as he had promised. She was careful not to drink too much of the wine, having heard lurid tales of its potency. But she trusted Steve, who didn't even attempt a pass. She wasn't too sure about herself, she thought wryly, feeling that she might be too encouraging too soon only to regret it later. Even a level-headed girl like herself could be swept off her feet by the combination of an attractive man and the reckless consumption of an unfamiliar drink!

They talked and laughed a lot. Gillian discovered that he liked the same books, the same music, the same kind of films as herself. She didn't play golf and he didn't dance, and they came from very different backgrounds, but those were minor flaws. Gillian didn't know if he was just being nice to a newcomer or if he really was interested. Nor did she know which way she wanted it at the moment. It was much too soon to commit herself to any kind of relationship—and no doubt he felt that, too. For there was only a warm, reassuring friendliness in his eyes and not even a hint of amorous intent.

Woman-like, Gillian didn't know whether to be glad or sorry.

Steve passed on some very useful information that evening about Greenvale and its staff, its many and varied types of cases, its rules and routines. For some reason, he didn't mention Mark Barlow—and Gillian was determined not to ask about the surgeon. She knew as much as she wanted to know, after all—and she didn't mean to let him intrude on a pleasant evening.

Just after eleven-thirty the doorbell pealed. Gillian was making coffee in the kitchen and she appeared in the doorway, pot in hand, rather startled and glad that Steve was with her. It was late for casual callers and she didn't know anyone who'd be likely to ring her bell at this hour, anyway. Living on her own in the heart of the town with its late-night revellers could have its disadvantages, she felt.

'Who on earth . . . ?'

'Oh, that'll be my chauffeur,' Steve said lightly, swinging long legs to the floor from the sofa where he had been lounging, entirely at his ease. 'My car's in for repair and I had to cadge a lift this evening.'

Gillian knew before she opened the door that it was Mark Barlow with an insistent finger on the bell. Typically impatient, she thought with dislike. She realised by the gleam of surprise in his eyes that her presence was unexpected. It seemed that Steve had chosen not to tell his friend that he was spending the evening at her flat.

'If you want to wake the dead, try the churchyard,' she said coolly. 'It's just across the road.' It wasn't friendly. She didn't mean it to be. She didn't like the look that had replaced the surprise in the grey eyes. She was suddenly conscious of the way that the silk kimono clung to every line of her slender body. She wondered why she hadn't felt at all self-conscious with Steve and why this beastly man should make her feel that she was deliberately parading her feminine attractions.

'Sorry. I'm looking for Steve.'

'You've found him.' She couldn't leave him standing

on the doorstep, much as she'd have liked to do so. She stepped to one side. 'You'd better come in.' She knew it was ungracious. She didn't care.

'Thank you.' He was very dry.

'We might even give you a cup of coffee,' Steve said in light-hearted greeting. 'Just made, isn't it, Gillian?'

'I'll get another cup.' It was said without warmth as she moved towards the kitchen.

Mark looked after her and then down at his friend, comfortably ensconced on the sofa in front of an ancient television set showing an equally ancient film. He never ceased to be amazed that Steve managed to score so quickly and without obvious trying with every pretty newcomer to the clinic. He had only met this girl that morning, apparently. Yet here he was, lounging about in her flat as though he owned the place and looking very well-pleased with himself. She hadn't been at all pleased to be caught in her dressing-gown, he thought wryly, feeling an odd flicker of dislike that she had obviously been a willing participant in Steve's amorous games.

Steve grinned at his friend and colleague, indicating a chair. 'Sit down, Mark. Make yourself at home!'

'I can see that *you* have,' he returned, dryly.

'She's a great girl,' Steve said warmly, unconscious of innuendo. 'I feel as if I've known her for ever.' He leaned forward to switch off the television set. 'How was your evening?'

'Very interesting.'

Gillian came back with the extra cup and poured coffee for the three of them as the surgeon gave Steve a brief résumé of the lecture on hypnotherapy he had attended that evening.

Genuinely interested, she asked one or two questions.

He answered impatiently as though he suspected her of merely making polite conversation. Gillian bridled. He ought to know by now that she found it extremely difficult to be polite where he was concerned, she thought indignantly, glowering.

Their eyes clashed across the room. She was annoyed with herself for being the first to look away. But there was an unexpected flame of angry contempt in the depths of those grey eyes. He really despised her, she realised with a sense of shock. It didn't matter in the least, of course. Didn't she despise him just as much? But no one likes to be weighed and found wanting by a stranger and Gillian found herself resenting that harsh, too-ready judgment.

He was the kind of man that any self-respecting woman would love to bring to his knees, she thought with feminine indignation, wishing that she knew how it was done! She didn't have the looks or the cool sophistication or the cleverness of a Louise Penistone—or a wealthy father to attract an ambitious man. He wasn't going to look twice at her, obviously, and he was the last man on earth that she would want as any kind of friend. But oh! she would dearly love to humble that proud and disdainful arrogance!

She made a point of not offering a second cup of coffee to either man. She was tired and she wanted her bed, and she wanted to be rid of Mark Barlow. His unexpected and unwelcome arrival had ruined everything, she felt. She had enjoyed the evening so much, the food and the wine, laughing and talking with Steve, mowing the lawn together with the ancient mower threatening to collapse on them at every push, watching the old Bogart movie as it flickered across the small screen. It had all been so innocent, so heart-warming. Then Mark Barlow had turned up to make her feel that there was something unacceptable about a girl spending an evening with a man she scarcely knew in the privacy and comfort of her flat. His manner implied that he suspected them of spending most of it in bed, she thought bitterly, hating him.

Steve took the hint and rose to his feet. 'You must be wishing us at Jericho,' he said lightly, smiling at her. 'It's late and I know you're tired. Mark and I have this tendency to talk all night when we get together but we mustn't do it here. We'll be off and let you get to bed, love.' At the door of the flat he bent to kiss her, friend rather than would-be lover, lips brushing her mouth so lightly that it was scarcely a kiss at all but it warmed her heart. 'It was a fantastic evening,' he said warmly. 'We must do it again.'

'Yes. We will. When the grass needs cutting again, perhaps,' she said, teasing him, smiling. She laid her hand along his cheek in an impulsive gesture of affection that had unconsciously endeared her to many men. 'Thanks—for everything.' Glancing at Mark Barlow, she saw that he watched them with a slight, mocking smile. She felt like throwing something at that handsome head. Her chin tilted. 'Goodnight,' she said coldly, meeting his eyes.

'Goodnight, Gillian,' he returned carelessly, turning away and striding towards his parked car.

She fumed. She hadn't made him a present of her first name! How dared he use it so casually—and how dared he walk away as though she didn't merit the common courtesies? He hadn't even thanked her for the coffee!

His Mercedes, gleaming opulently in the light from a

street lamp, was parked just behind her Mini, almost touching its rear bumper. Worlds apart and with nothing in common—just as they were and would always remain, she realised.

She watched the competent economy of his movements as he produced car keys, opened the door and swung himself behind the wheel. He turned on the ignition then leaned across to open the passenger door for Steve.

Gillian waved goodnight. Only Steve responded with a cheerful wave of his hand and his ready smile. Mark Barlow had already dismissed her, she knew.

As the Mercedes drew smoothly away from the kerb, she went back into the flat and closed and locked the door.

The rooms seemed empty as she went from one to the other, clearing away the coffee cups and rinsing them beneath the running tap, tidying the living-room and kitchen, securing the windows, getting ready for bed. Steve wasn't a big man by any means but he had seemed to fill the place with his warm, extrovert personality. It was absurd but she missed him already.

She continued to think about Steve as she undressed and brushed her pale hair into a silky cloud about her head, then climbed between the sheets of the wide double bed. He was a dear. She liked him so much. He hadn't put a foot wrong all evening. Gillian hoped that he liked her just as much and felt reasonably confident that he did, recalling the smile in his eyes and the warmth in his voice and the way he had kissed her on parting. That kiss had been a promise for the future, she decided with satisfaction.

Resolutely thinking about Steve as she put out the

bedside light and snuggled down, she didn't know why such a vivid image of Mark Barlow should be stubbornly etched on her closed eyelids for all her efforts to thrust it aside and go to sleep.

A handsome, sensual face with its strongly sculptured features and deep-set eyes and mobile mouth, spoiled for Gillian by the sardonic expression, the cold smile and the haughty lift of an eyebrow. But, remembering the way that he had smiled and looked at the lovely Louise Penistone, she could believe that he might be very attractive to women.

He dressed too formally for her liking although she admitted that he looked well in his obviously expensive clothes. But she preferred Steve's casual and comfortable appearance. He wore his dark, crisply curling hair a little too long, she thought critically, seeing in her mind's eye the impatient hand brushing it back from his brow in an habitual gesture while he talked. The best thing about Mark Barlow was his hands. They had impressed her.

Strong, sensitive, capable—they were surgeon's hands. Competent hands, inspiring confidence. Hands that would always know exactly what to do, whether wielding a scalpel to save a life or moving across a woman's body in experienced caress.

Gillian jerked her thoughts to a halt, slightly shocked that they had wandered in such a dangerous direction. She might admire Mark Barlow's hands but she had not the slightest desire to know the touch of them on any part of her body, with or without a scalpel!

She didn't know him. She didn't want to know him. But she had the uncomfortable conviction that he wasn't a forgettable man. If only because he roused her to a degree of dislike and loathing such as she had never felt for anyone before.

It was mutual, she knew. It was as much as he could do to be civil to her—and so far he hadn't tried very hard.

Gillian was a warm-hearted girl. She liked people very readily as a rule. But it was impossible to like someone as insufferable as Mark Barlow, with his exalted opinion of himself and his scornful opinion of her as a mere nurse who had yet to prove her ability to his satisfaction.

CHAPTER FOUR

THE second day at Greenvale was much more enjoyable. Gillian found herself slipping easily into the routine and feeling more at ease with the other nurses who were beginning to accept her now that they found she was an efficient and cheerful worker as well as a friendly girl. She had shaken off the new-girl feeling.

She didn't see Steve. She had no occasion to visit Theatre and he apparently had no reason to come down to the floor where she was working. Gillian didn't mind that he made no attempt to see her, she didn't feel that it was a deliberate policy. He might not be on duty that day. Mark Barlow wasn't operating and it seemed that they usually worked together as a team.

Mrs Maddox was still on the monitor. She was making good progress but she was reacting to a routine pain-killing drug with some excitability. Naturally a jolly woman, buoyed up by morphine, she was making little of her obvious discomfort and was ready to turn every-thing into a huge joke.

Having spent a lively half-hour with the big woman, giving her a blanket-bath and making her as comfortable as possible for drip and drainage tubes and electrodes, and trying to calm her with very little success, Gillian emerged from the room, dark-blue eyes sparkling with suppressed merriment from some of the outrageous things that Mrs Maddox had been saying. She almost collided with Mark Barlow.

'Oops! Sorry!' she declared gaily, hastily swerving the
trolley out of his path before realising that the tall man in
the dark suit was the surgeon. He regarded her with a
sardonic lift of an eyebrow, disapproval in the grey eyes.
'Oh, it's you,' she said without enthusiasm.

His eyes narrowed at the sudden change of tone. 'I
don't think you are going to be an asset to this place,' he
said coldly, glancing through the open door at his patient
who was flushed and bright-eyed and beaming, obviously over-stimulated. He had heard the loud voice and
gusts of painful laughter as he strode along the corridor
and had wondered what on earth was going on in Room
Four. 'One would think that you know nothing at all
about post-operative nursing,' he swept on angrily. 'I
believe I stressed that Mrs Maddox was to be kept very
quiet for a few days. She's a very excitable woman with a
history of hypertension. Things must have changed con-
siderably at St Christopher's if its nurses behave like
third-rate music-hall entertainers instead of doing their
work in an orderly manner and having proper care for
their patients!''

Without giving her a chance to defend herself, or
explain the reason for Mrs Maddox's excitability, he
strode into the room. Gillian was speechless with indignation anyway. She glared at his broad and totally
uncompromising back as he stood at the foot of the bed,
chart in hand, talking in clipped tones to his patient.

He had been deliberately offensive. Gillian trundled
the trolley along to the clinical room seething, her heart
pounding with hatred, on the point of rushing off to the
office with her notice. She simply couldn't work with
such a man. It was more than flesh and blood could
stand. He didn't have a good word for her. He had the

lowest possible opinion of her nursing ability. He didn't like her at all and took every opportunity to be unpleasant.

Automatically, she cleared the trolley and put things away, hands shaking with suppressed fury. Penny Hughes entered the clinical room and sent her a sympathetic smile, having heard every word. She had been busy in the adjoining room, getting it ready for a new occupant. 'That was quite a slamming. What *did* you do?' she asked lightly.

'Absolutely nothing,' Gillian said bitterly.

Penny raised an eyebrow. 'He's quick but he's usually fair.'

'Not where I'm concerned. To hear him, you'd think I'd been dancing on the ceiling and swinging from the chandelier instead of doing my best to restrain Mrs Maddox from attempting much the same things!'

'She's high on morphine, isn't she? Why didn't you explain?'

Gillian threw her a sceptical glance. 'I didn't get the chance—and when he'd finished wiping the floor with me I didn't have the inclination.'

Penny laughed. 'I don't think you like him very much.'

'Not at all! And he doesn't like me. It's mutual antipathy.' Gillian was very angry. His scathing words were still ringing in her ears. Her heart was hammering and she felt quite sick, her legs were jelly. She was suddenly very cold and trembly. Her head swam and she clutched at the bench for support. Penny turned to her, concerned. Through a thickening mist, she heard the girl's voice asking if she was all right. She couldn't answer. She was falling, falling . . .

*

Gillian came round as she was being lifted by strong arms and laid none too gently on a couch in the clinical room.

'Sal volatile!'

She seemed to know that impatient voice. She turned away her head, murmuring protest, hating the pungency of the salts. But they were effective and her head began to clear. She opened her eyes to see Mark Barlow bending over her, fingers on the pulse in her neck. She struggled with the confusion of her thoughts, oddly determined that she wouldn't come out with the traditional 'where am I?'

'I'm all right,' she said lamely. He was much too near. She was too conscious of penetrating grey eyes and a grim expression. She was too aware of his physical presence. Instinctively she put out her hands to push him away. He caught and held them. In her muddled state of mind, his hands seemed to throb with power and passion. He was angry, she realised, surprised. Because she had been silly enough to faint? Why *had* she fainted? She was perfectly well. 'Could I have some water?'

Penny brought it. 'Feeling better?' she asked kindly.

Gillian sat up, drank some of the ice-cold water and felt the faintness receding. 'Yes, thanks . . .'

Perhaps she had returned to work too soon, she thought ruefully. But it hadn't been possible to save much out of her salary and she was too independent to seek financial help from her parents. She might have managed for a few more weeks but she had hated to see her small reserves dwindling and the job at Greenvale had seemed opportune. Private nursing paid so well. She was really quite fit, she thought proudly. She had merely been doing too much. And the strongly emotional reaction to yet another clash with a man she particularly disliked and who could infuriate her without even trying had just been the last straw.

'I know you're busy, Penny.' Mark had seen the girl's quick glance at her watch. 'I'll take care of Gillian if you want to get on.'

'Well, Miss Wilmot *is* due for her injection.' Penny smiled at him, very warm. 'And you *are* a doctor, after all!'

She hurried from the room.

Thoughtful, Mark surveyed the girl on the couch who was much too pale and wouldn't meet his eyes.

'Are you pregnant?' he asked abruptly.

The brusque words shocked Gillian into full consciousness. She threw up her head and glared at him. 'No, I'm not!'

The negation was so fierce, so vehement, that he blinked. 'Just a thought,' he drawled soothingly. 'It happens.'

'Not to me, it doesn't,' she told him coldly.

The merest glimmer of a smile came and went in the grey eyes at that proud retort. 'Then we'd better have you checked out,' he decided. 'Healthy young women don't make a practice of fainting all over the place.'

'I don't make a practice of it, either,' Gillian retorted indignantly. 'That's a typically male exaggeration and just what I'd expect from you!' She swung her feet to the floor and stood up. She was a trifle unsteady at first but she moved pointedly away from the hovering hand that threatened to assist her. 'I'm fine now,' she said with a touch of defiance.

'I shall ask Dr Howard to run the rule over you,

nevertheless,' Mark said firmly, referring to one of the staff physicians.

'There's no need for that. I've just had a medical. I daresay I've been overdoing things. I had pneumonia and pleurisy, rather badly. Two months ago,' Gillian told him grudgingly, strangely reluctant to admit even the slightest weakness to this unsympathetic man. She was proud. He didn't make allowances for anyone. She didn't want him to make allowances for her—*ever*! 'I've been passed as fit but it's been a hectic week. Too much too soon, I expect.' She managed a cool smile.

He studied her with impersonal, entirely professional interest as she took the tumbler to the sink and rinsed it out carefully. 'I didn't like the look of you last night,' he said bluntly, remembering her air of fragility in that absurd kimono, her marked pallor and the violet smudges beneath her rather lovely eyes. He was not an impressionable man. It was odd that he seemed to have a very vivid impression of this slight, pretty girl with her delicate face and figure etched on his mind's eye. Her very Nordic looks had been strangely emphasised by the exotic kimono and the ridiculous spray of flowers against her pale hair, he recalled.

Gillian shot him an angry glance. 'So I noticed!' She was tart. It still rankled that he had looked her over with such obvious disapproval and contempt, making her feel cheap and promiscuous when she was nothing of the kind. She didn't care what he thought of her but he didn't have to show it so plainly!

He brushed aside glance and words with an impatience that didn't endear him to her. Nor did his next words. 'Steve is a likeable fellow but very thoughtless,' he said brusquely. 'Don't allow him to use you, Gillian.'

She bridled instinctively. '*Use me . . . ?*' she echoed icily. 'What does that mean? And don't call me Gillian!'

'He'll treat your place as his second home if you let him,' he elaborated, dismissing the angry rider as a sign that she was overwrought. Greenvale was an informal, friendly place and all the staff were on first-name terms out of hearing of the patients. Did she expect him to call her *Nurse* or *Miss Grant* when they would be working together for the next year, for heaven's sake? Mark had no patience with that kind of false pride.

Gillian struggled to keep the simmering anger from boiling over again. He was a poisonous creature, she thought fiercely, indignant on Steve's behalf as he wasn't there to defend himself. She didn't think that the surgeon could be jealous of the instant rapport that had sprung to life between herself and Steve but he obviously disapproved of it—and he was using a particularly sneaky kind of venom in an attempt to spoil their newfound friendship.

She *liked* Steve's easy ways, his readiness to slip into her life as if he had always belonged in it. She was perfectly happy for him to treat her flat as his second home if he wished to do so, she thought defiantly. She might even ask him to move in with her eventually if affection turned to loving—as it might. Damn Mark Barlow!

'Anything else?' she asked bitingly.

He smiled, sardonic. 'Do you want to hear that he'll drop you as soon as someone more attractive or with more to offer comes along? I doubt it. The danger with Steve is that he never means to hurt anyone. He's so casual and so selfish that it just doesn't occur to him that he takes all the time and doesn't give much in return. He's entirely amoral.'

'I don't believe you,' Gillian said flatly.

He shrugged, annoyed. He didn't usually involve himself in this way with any of Steve's many and varied girlfriends. He didn't know why he should be concerned for Gillian Grant, with her prickly pride and stubborn hostility. He didn't even like the girl. That air of fragility and innocence was bound to be deceptive. She could probably take good care of herself. And if she couldn't— well, it was nothing to do with him, he told himself impatiently.

'I don't know why I'm bothering to warn you. Girls like you ask for everything they get, I'm afraid,' he said carelessly.

At that, Gillian swung round and slapped him hard. She saw the pain and the fury leap into his grey eyes and felt sudden alarm. She stepped back, frightened by her own violent reaction to his words. In all her life she had never raised a hand to anyone in temper. She was a gentle, warm-hearted girl who had never known what it meant to hate until she met Mark Barlow. She hated him with a surprising degree of passion.

'Tears next, I expect,' he drawled, eyes glinting with cold anger. 'Then you'll have run the whole gamut. My God, you're a credit to that Kit's badge, aren't you?' He was contemptuous, furious. 'We can do without nurses like you at Greenvale!'

'I'm not sorry.'

She threw the words at him defiantly, forcing back the tears that were stinging her eyes. She would *not* give him the satisfaction of seeing her cry, she thought fiercely. She *wasn't* sorry. He deserved that slap. He had been asking for it since their first encounter.

'You're a child,' he told her coldly, with dislike. She would have slapped him again, bristling, but he caught her wrist. 'Control yourself!' he commanded. She drew a deep, choking breath. He saw that she was trembling, ashen-fashed, tears of anger brimming in the huge blue eyes. 'Come on,' he said, more gently, giving her a little shake. 'That's enough—pull yourself together, Gillian. If I said too much, I'm sorry.' Her eyes widened. A slight smile tugged at his lips, sternly repressed. 'Oh, *I'm* not too proud to be in the wrong or to apologise,' he drawled.

Gillian pulled her wrist free, rubbing it where his strong fingers had gripped the soft flesh. She tingled all over from his touch, from the smouldering passion that he was man enough to master while she had given way to a flame of fury.

She glowered at him. Then she turned away, tugging at her apron, straightening her cap. 'I've work to do.'

'No.' It was quiet but firm. 'You're in no state to deal with patients.' He looked at his watch. 'I've an hour to spare. I'll take you home. Get your things while I explain to Mary Kenny.'

His tone didn't allow for argument. But Gillian wasn't going to take orders from him. 'I can take myself home, thanks,' she said promptly, proudly. She didn't insist that she was well enough to go on with her work. She knew that she wasn't. 'My car's outside . . .'

'How do I know you won't collapse at the wheel? You don't look fit to drive.' He was blunt.

'Then I'll take a taxi.' Her chin lifted.

'I wish you wouldn't argue,' he said with sudden impatience. 'I know where you live and it won't take ten minutes. I don't like the look of you.'

'So you keep saying,' she said bitterly.

He looked at her in surprise.

Gillian hurried from the room, furious that she had been goaded into saying something that he would probably misconstrue. She hadn't meant that the way it had sounded. She didn't want him to like her looks or anything else about her. She didn't want him to think of her as a woman, attractive or otherwise. She might find herself thinking of him as a man, she thought wryly, shocked that in the midst of their wrangling she had known a tingling excitement, a sexual awareness of his potent masculinity. He was very much a man, she thought, with a flutter of alarm that it was possible to be physically stirred by a man she disliked and despised. It was absurd, she told herself hastily, something to be thrust to the back of her mind and forgotten.

But it had happened . . .

He was waiting for her with Mary Kenny outside the administrator's office. Mary cast a concerned eye over Gillian's slender figure as she approached. Perhaps it wasn't conscious but she was immediately indignant, knowing that the elderly woman was also wondering if she was pregnant. She felt like declaring hotly that women *had* been known to faint for lots of other reasons!

'I'm sorry to hear that you aren't well, Miss Grant,' Mary said, kind but irritated that the girl should have returned to nursing before she was fully recovered from an illness. *If* that was the real reason for the faint. One never knew with these modern girls with their promiscuous behaviour and careless disregard for the consequences . . .

'Thank you. It was only a faint,' Gillian said defensively. 'But Mr Barlow insists on taking me home—quite unnecessarily, I think. I shall be perfectly all right for work tomorrow.'

'Well, I hope so, my dear. This is most unfortunate when you've only just joined us . . .' The words trailed off on a sigh. The telephone rang in her office and she hurried to answer it.

Gillian bit her lip. 'She thinks I'm pregnant, too.'

Mark shrugged. 'You're too sensitive. What does it matter, anyway? As long as you know you're not.'

'I do!' she said sharply.

He took her bag from her hand as they left the clinic and began to make their way towards the car park.

'I'm not an invalid,' she protested, trying to recapture her property.

'I'm a gentleman,' he drawled. 'Why don't you pretend to be a lady?'

'Pig!' she snapped, hot with anger.

He laughed, soft and mocking. Gillian looked at him with dislike. He put a hand on her arm to check her as a car's tyres scrunched on the gravel behind them, turning into the car park. She shook it off fiercely. He didn't seem to notice the rebuff.

Pausing at the sleek Mercedes, gleaming in the afternoon sun, Gillian glanced across at her own little Mini doubtfully. She loved it but it was beginning to look very battered after years of competing with the heavy London traffic and it did need a respray. She wished she could afford it.

'What about my car?' she asked.

He didn't even look at it. 'It'll be fine. Don't worry about it,' he said dismissively, producing his car keys. 'Anyone who went off with it would only be doing you a favour.'

'It suits me,' she said defensively. 'I shall miss it in the morning.'

He opened the passenger door, helped her into the seat with careless courtesy. 'No, you won't. I'll call for you. It's on my way.' He closed the door, walked round to the other side of the car and slid behind the wheel.

Gillian was puzzled. 'How can it be?' she demanded. 'Aren't you a resident? Like Steve?'

'Only occasionally.' He turned on the ignition and the car responded immediately. 'I was on call last night, for instance. That's how I was able to oblige Steve when he wanted a lift to your place and back. But I have a house of my own, you know, on the other side of town.'

She lapsed into silence. She would have liked to ask a thousand questions but he was not the kind of man to welcome them, she felt. She sat stiffly by his side while he drove towards the town, her head carefully turned to watch the passing scenery, determined not to be impressed by the comfort, the elegance and the opulence of the Mercedes, such a contrast to her shabby and none too reliable Mini.

He didn't seem aware of her silence, her refusal to relax. He reached for a cassette and slotted it into the player, switched on. Music filled the car, sweet and low, the kind of music she particularly liked. She glanced at him. He kept his attention on the road, hands light but capable on the wheel as the car steadily consumed the miles.

With a little shock of guilt, Gillian saw the marks of her fingers on his lean, bronzed cheek. Faint but unmistakably the result of a slap. The weals had been flaming just after she had hit him, still very much in evidence when he went off to talk to Mary Kenny. She wondered if the woman had noticed, commented—and how he had explained them away!

Somehow, she didn't think that he was the kind of man to give explanations for anything to anyone. He probably didn't give much away at all, in fact. He seemed so cold, so reserved, so remote—and he was the most arrogant man she had ever known.

He ran a hand through his dark hair as they paused at traffic lights. Gillian noticed the tight black curls on the nape of his neck and suspected that they were brushed out of existence each morning only to leap back to life during the day. Unruly curls didn't go with the smooth, controlled good looks of a Mark Barlow, after all, she thought dryly. He *was* good-looking. Physically, he was a very attractive man. Tall, lean but muscular, there was an animal magnetism about him that was very potent . . .

He turned his head suddenly. Gillian realised that she was staring. She looked away, a hint of colour creeping into her small face. Her slender hands suddenly locked in her lap with the apprehensive conviction that he had known just what she was thinking and just where those thoughts were leading her.

The car moved forward smoothly. Within moments, it had turned into the narrow street and drawn up to the kerb outside the dilapidated Victorian villa that housed her flat.

Mark turned to Gillian.

'I won't come in . . .'

'Don't bother to come in . . .'

They spoke in unison, Gillian slightly flustered, Mark coolly casual. His mouth tightened at the obvious dis-

trust of her manner. She smiled with quick and obliga-
tory gratitude.

'I'll be fine now,' she said, although he didn't give the
impression of caring one way or the other.

'Get some rest,' he advised indifferently.

'Yes . . . yes, I will.' She reached for her bag.

'Sleeping properly?'

Gillian hesitated. 'Not too well.'

'Have you any tablets?'

'No—and I don't want them. There isn't anything
wrong. It's just—oh, nervousness, I think.' She smiled
ruefully. 'Being alone in the flat. I know it sounds silly
but I'm not used to it. Since I left home, I've always
shared with someone.'

He studied her thoughtfully, wondering if the 'someone' had been a man, wondering what brought a girl like
this to a small country town, miles from all her friends
and everything she knew. She had latched on to Steve so
quickly that she might be looking for a replacement for a
lost lover. She was a pretty girl and just the type to
appeal to Steve. But she wouldn't find him any more
reliable than the last one, he thought dryly.

'I expect you'll soon find someone to share with you
again,' he said coolly. 'In the meantime, I don't think
you need to be nervous. We're a very law-abiding lot in
this part of the world.'

As the car drew away, Gillian looked after it, wondering why she had been prompted to confide in someone so
obviously indifferent to her anxieties or problems. He
was the most unfeeling man she had ever met!

CHAPTER FIVE

THE telephone rang while Gillian was in the bath. She snatched a thick towel, wrapped it about her slender body and stepped out of the steaming, fragrant water, hurrying to answer the shrill summons before the caller rang off. She wondered if it might be Mark. He had driven away earlier without arranging a time to call for her the next morning.

It was Steve.

'Steve!' she said, pleased but surprised. 'I didn't think you knew the number.'

'Mary Kenny obliged. How are you? I gather that you collapsed in Mark's arms this afternoon?'

'Is that the story?' Her tone was dry. 'It wasn't quite like that.'

'Are you all right?'

'Yes, of course. It was just a faint. Nothing to worry about.' *Don't ask if I'm pregnant or even hint at it*, she pleaded silently, fervently.

He didn't. 'Is there anything I can do? Would you like me to come over? Officially, I'm on call but I can probably twist Jeff's arm. He owes me a favour.'

'I'm fine. Really.' Gillian was reassuring.

'I don't like to think of you on your own, love.'

She was touched by the warmth of his concern, by the hint of affection in the casual endearment. 'I'm going to climb into bed with a book. Don't worry,' she said firmly.

He gave a gusty sigh. 'What a terrible waste of your youth. You ought to be climbing into bed with a good-looking man—preferably me!'

Gillian chuckled. 'Mark Barlow brought me home. Did you know?' she said on a sudden impulse.

There was a moment's silence. Then he said carefully: 'Is there a connection?'

She was puzzled. Then, 'Oh, I see what you mean! No, of course not. I just thought I'd mention it.' She was glad that he couldn't see the heat in her face as she realised the implication of his words.

'It isn't news. Everyone knows. You seem to have made quite an impression on our Mark,' he said lightly.

Gillian knew she had been naive not to realise that Greenvale had a grapevine that was just as busy as the one that carried all the intimate details of everyone's affairs at Kit's. She wondered dryly what everyone was making of an affair that just didn't exist. But she had certainly given the gossips plenty to talk about by quarrelling openly with Mark Barlow and then driving off with him in his sleek Mercedes. Even *she* found it difficult to believe that she had never met the man until yesterday, she thought dryly.

'I think he meant to be kind,' she said, rather stiffly.

'And who could blame him? You're a lovely girl,' Steve told her warmly. 'But nurses aren't much in his line, as a rule. He's more of a high-flyer. His women usually have a touch of class.'

'And nurses haven't?' There was a sudden edge to her voice.

'Ouch!' he said ruefully.

She could almost see the grin that lit up his pleasant face and blue eyes. She liked him too much to take offence at a moment's thoughtlessness, she decided. She relaxed. 'It's all right. I know what you mean,' she said tolerantly.

She thought of Louise Penistone. A casual comment to Penny had elicited a description that matched the girl she had seen with Mark Barlow. A touch of class indeed, she thought now. Everything about the girl had shouted money—looks, clothes, manner. Gillian didn't doubt that she was just the kind of woman to attract an ambitious and successful surgeon who didn't bother with mere nurses . . .

'Me . . . I *like* nurses,' Steve announced generously.

Gillian laughed. 'I'm glad to hear it.'

'I like you, Gillian.' It was low, tender.

She didn't know what to say. She didn't want him turning serious . . . not yet, perhaps not at all.

'I was in the bath,' she said uncertainly.

'Then you're getting chilled! Sorry, love. I'll ring off.'

'I'm glad you phoned, Steve.'

She didn't go back to the bath although she had planned a long, lazy soak. She was warmed by Steve's call yet vaguely troubled by it. He seemed to be getting very involved, she thought unhappily. She liked him so much. She would hate having to hurt him.

It didn't occur to her that she might become equally involved given time, and that then there would be no question of hurting him, disappointing his obvious hopes. For some reason, she knew instinctively that Steve just wasn't her destiny . . .

Mark didn't telephone.

She was ready and waiting when he called at the flat the next morning. She had been feeling anxious, wondering if he had meant the careless words and how she would get to the clinic if he didn't turn up.

'You're here!' she exclaimed, a trifle foolishly, as she opened the door in answer to the ring at the bell.

He raised an eyebrow. 'In the flesh.'

'I mean . . . I didn't know—I wasn't sure . . .' She floundered.

'I said I'd call for you.'

'It was a bit vague.'

'It was quite definite, I thought.' His tone was uncompromising.

She realised that he was annoyed. She had implied that he was unreliable, perhaps. She hadn't meant it that way.

'Yes. But you didn't mention times . . .' She tried to explain.

'You won't be late. It only takes fifteen minutes, allowing for traffic.' He looked her over. 'How are you?'

It sounded like an afterthought. But Gillian admitted fairly that he had no reason to care about her health. Considering that they weren't friends and never could be, it had been kind of him to bring her home and it was even kinder that he had kept his promise to call for her that morning.

'Fine . . . I'm fine,' she said stoutly.

Mark tilted her chin with strong fingers to examine the small, delicately pretty face. He saw that there was colour in the cheeks and less of a shadow beneath the eyes. He saw that she stiffened, too. He saw the dark blue eyes flash with sudden dislike at his touch. He frowned.

She moved away from him. 'I know you're a doctor.

But you're not *my* doctor,' she said sharply. 'I'm perfectly well, I tell you.' She picked up bag and keys. 'And I'm ready. Shall we go?'

His touch had been impersonal. Like too many women, she had immediately assumed an interest that just didn't exist, he thought impatiently, following her to the car . . .

Gillian knew that she had snapped unfairly. But she hadn't been prepared for that hand beneath her chin—or for what his touch did to her, she thought wryly. She marvelled that her body could react so swiftly to a man she hated, heart and soul. But the quivering little flame that had shot through her seemed to have no connection with liking or respect or friendship or anything but an out-and-out wanting that was entirely physical. She had known a fierce throb of excitement at the thought of his arms about her and his powerful body urgent against her own—and rejected it with all her might.

She sat as far from him in the car as she could, not risking even the casual brushing of his hand across her sleeve. She was so afraid that he might sense the sudden and alarming arousal which had shocked her virgin body into a new awareness of sexual attraction.

She took refuge in talking about the clinic, about Kit's. 'It's where you qualified, isn't it?' He nodded. 'When? I mean—I don't remember you at all.'

'I'm flattered that you should suppose I'd be particularly memorable,' he said dryly. 'Kit's turns out doctors by the score.'

Gillian flushed. He made it very difficult for her to warm to him, she thought resentfully. 'Am I prying? Sorry.' She was stiff.

'It's over five years since I last worked at Kit's. I was

senior registrar on John Harcourt's team,' he said, referring to a well known gynaecological surgeon.

'I was a first-year five years ago. We just missed each other,' she said without regret.

'Just as well, don't you think? Kit's doesn't approve of junior nurses who assault surgeons.' He rubbed his cheek reminiscently as he spoke.

'And I expect you were just as insufferable in those days,' she agreed sweetly, with spirit.

Mark glanced at her with a glimmer of laughter in his eyes. 'I daresay you'd have thought so. You make up your mind about people very quickly, don't you?'

Gillian missed the laughter, heard only the censure. 'And I'm never wrong!' she declared proudly, sure that he was referring to her instant friendship with Steve.

'Then you're fortunate. I find that I'm constantly having to adjust my thinking about people,' he drawled. 'In my experience, first impressions can be not only unreliable but dangerous.'

Gillian fancied that he was warning her again about trusting Steve. She bridled. She liked Steve and she was sure that she could safely follow her instincts where he was concerned—and it was none of Mark Barlow's business if she was mistaken.

'Men don't have the advantage of feminine intuition,' she said sweepingly.

'Men don't tumble into love at first sight, if that's what you mean.' He was scathing. 'In fact, love as women know it just doesn't exist for men, I'm afraid. We're too hard-headed, too practical. Women refuse to be realists and cling to a ridiculous dream of romance and happy-ever-after.'

'I wasn't talking about love!' she exclaimed, indignant, hoping with all her heart that one day some woman would cause him to regret bitterly those arrogant words. 'I'm talking of liking, trust, understanding. But I doubt if any of those things come easily to *you*!'

'No,' he agreed smoothly, amused rather than offended by her bluntness. 'But when I do care for someone it lasts, Gillian. Flash-in-the-pan affairs have never been my style.'

'You strike me as a very cold-blooded man,' she said bluntly, with dislike.

'But you don't know me very well, do you?' He was carelessly indifferent to her opinion. They had reached Greenvale, gracious and attractive in the morning sunshine. He drove the car through the wide gates with a wave of his hand for the lodgekeeper.

'And I don't particularly want to know you any better!' Gillian flashed, goaded by the lazy drawl into outright rudeness.

'Is that temper or truth, I wonder?' He brought the car to a halt in the car park and switched off the engine. He turned to her, smiling. 'Shall I put that claim to the test?'

'Try me!' she invited hotly, annoyed that he obviously doubted her dislike, her indifference. Did he think he had only to turn on the charm, to smile in a certain way, for her to change her mind about him? He was wrong!

He was silent, studying her.

Her chin tilted. She didn't like the cool confidence, the faint gleam of mockery in the grey eyes that commanded her own gaze so imperiously. He was much too sure of himself.

She didn't like his closeness in the confines of the car. She was much too conscious of his maleness, his sexual challenge to her senses. Her heart began to thud. But she looked back at him steadily, defiant, prickly with pride.

For a moment, the atmosphere was electric.

Then he shook his head.

'I don't like militant women,' he declared coolly, reaching to the back seat for her bag and handing it to her.

Keyed up to the point of being ready to slap him again if he made any attempt to kiss her, suspecting it was in his mind, Gillian was abruptly deflated by his dismissive tone and manner.

'Naturally you'd prefer the downtrodden door-mat type who gazes adoringly at you and says yes to every-thing and wouldn't dream of criticising you,' she said scornfully, getting out of the car.

She didn't wait for him. She set off towards the big house, head high. With a few of his long strides, he caught up with her.

'Any man would prefer a gentle, sweet-natured girl who wouldn't dream of walking away without so much as a thank you for a lift,' he agreed dryly.

The colour swept into Gillian's face. She looked up at him quickly, defensively. 'Yes, that was rude of me,' she admitted readily, unable to be anything but honest. 'I'm sorry. Thank you for the lift.'

'"*I'm very grateful*",' he prompted.

She shot him a baleful glance. 'I'm very grateful,' she echoed stiffly. 'But it wasn't necessary, you know. I could have taken a taxi or caught a bus.'

He sighed, irritated. 'I didn't *have* to call for you, Gillian. No one twisted my arm. Believe it or not, I was concerned about you. I wanted to check for myself that you were fit enough for work.'

'Perhaps you hoped to catch me in the throes of morning sickness,' she said dryly, unfairly. 'You just aren't convinced that I'm not pregnant, are you?'

He stopped and looked down at her, suddenly angry. 'I don't give a damn if you're about to go into labour. What an aggressive, unpleasant girl you are! Heaven knows what Steve finds to like in you! I should think everyone at Kit's must have breathed a sigh of relief when you left!'

Gillian felt as though he had struck her, so forceful were the words and the contempt behind them. Suddenly, foolishly, she wanted to cry. But being proud, she glowered at him instead.

A fair, stocky young man had driven through the gates of Greenvale behind the Mercedes and left his own car in the visitors' parking area. He had walked behind them as they approached the building in obvious argument and now he glanced curiously at the couple as he drew level, knowing the surgeon well and wondering about his fair companion who seemed vaguely familiar.

He looked more closely, paused.

'Gillian?' he exclaimed doubtfully, quite sure of her identity, but not at all sure how she would react to seeing him.

She turned, coming alive with eager delight at the sound of a familiar voice. 'Robin!'

'Gillian . . .' He was more confident, just as delighted, smiling at her warmly.

Mark felt like an intruder, observing the transformation from glowering rebellion to glowing pleasure at this obviously unexpected reunion of old friends . . . and perhaps more than friends, he thought shrewdly, noting her shining eyes and the warmth of McAllister's smile.

He doubted that Steve would be too happy to hear that his new fancy and a local GP seemed to have something going for each other.

'How lovely to see you!' Gillian exclaimed warmly, meaning it with all her heart.

Robin held her hand very tightly. 'I don't believe it's really you! What are you doing here?'

'What about *you*? What are you doing here?' she countered, smiling.

Mark decided it was time to leave them to their explanations. Neither of them seemed to be aware any longer of his existence, he thought dryly. He laid a light hand on the man's shoulder. 'On your way to see me, aren't you? I'll be in my office when you're ready.'

Robin looked at him blankly for a moment. Then he nodded, smiled. 'Sorry! I didn't mean to be rude. But I haven't seen Gillian in much too long! I'll be with you in ten minutes.'

Mark nodded. 'Don't overdo things today, Gillian,' he said brusquely, sounding like her medical adviser, and strode away.

She looked after him briefly. Then she turned to Robin, gazing at him as if he had stepped out of a dream. As he had!

It was three years since they had last seen each other. Three years of remembering him with warm affection and even at times half regretting her decision not to marry him. But, three years before, she had been in the middle of her training and enjoying every moment of it and she just hadn't been ready to commit herself to anything as irrevocable as marriage.

About to leave Kit's and join an uncle in general practice somewhere in Sussex, Robin had taken it for granted that she would marry him and settle down happily as a doctor's wife and give up all thought of her nursing career. But Gillian hadn't wanted to leave Kit's and all her friends and all the fun. Frankly, she just hadn't been sufficiently in love with Robin.

Now, smiling at him, knowing that her heart had lifted at the sight of him, she wondered if she had loved him more than she knew, had missed him more than she realised until a moment ago when she turned to see his dear, familiar face. Certainly she had been fond of him. Certainly they had been very close. Certainly she had been tempted by his proposal of marriage.

'But you're working here!' he exclaimed in surprise, belatedly realising that she was dressed in the Greenvale uniform. 'I thought you were still at Kit's!'

They had kept vaguely in touch throughout the years. The occasional letter or card, one or two telephone calls, news of each other through mutual friends. But she had hurt him badly and it had seemed that he didn't want to meet her again and Gillian had understood, hoping that he would soon get over her and eventually find someone who wouldn't hurt and disappoint him.

She shook her head, smiling. 'I left a couple of months ago.' There would be plenty of time and opportunity to explain everything to him, she felt. 'I've only been here for a few days. I never expected to run into you!'

'I'm in practice with my uncle,' he reminded her levelly. 'It's a group practice based in a health centre in the town. I thought that you knew.' There was the faintest hint of reproach that she should have forgotten his plans on leaving Kit's after qualifying.

Of course she had known! Gillian marvelled that it could have slipped her memory so completely. Ever since she had applied for the job at Greenvale there had been a vague idea at the back of her mind that she had reason to know the name of the town where it was situated. How could she have forgotten that it was the very place where she would have lived with Robin if she had married him?

'Then you aren't associated with the clinic? Professionally, I mean?' She skated carefully over that hurtful lapse of memory.

Robin smiled down at her warmly, happily, ready to forgive her anything in the delight of this unexpected meeting. She had been so often in his thoughts. Why should he assume that someone as pretty and popular as Gillian should have had the time or the inclination to think about him as much?

'Oh, we send the occasional private patient along for treatment or surgery. It has a very good reputation. But how does it come about that you're here? Isn't it very dull in comparison with Kit's?'

'I haven't found it dull,' she said with truth. 'But it's early days, of course. I haven't yet found my feet. Or convinced anyone that I'm indispensable,' she added lightly, glancing at her watch. 'My track record is pretty poor to date and I mustn't be late this morning—and you've an appointment with Mark Barlow, apparently?'

As they walked on, he held firmly to her hand, reluctant to relinquish the physical contact with the girl he still loved. All his former feelings for her had surged through him at sight of her. Three years of learning to live without her had been swept away in a moment.

She smiled at him, warm and friendly, obviously pleased that they had met again. But there was a vague disquiet in Robin's heart.

'You're friends—you and Barlow?'

He put the question carefully. If she had forgotten that he lived and worked in the same town, if she had virtually forgotten him as seemed all too likely, then something else had brought her to work at Greenvale. Something more important than the hospital career which had meant so much to her and someone more important than he had ever been. Loving could be that something—and Mark Barlow could be that someone, he thought heavily.

'No,' Gillian said promptly, lightly. 'We only met a few days ago.'

Robin was reassured. He squeezed her hand. 'I thought you were quarrelling,' he told her, amused by his readiness to leap to absurd conclusions.

'Oh, we were. We do it all the time,' she said carelessly. 'We don't like each other.'

'He isn't the easiest man in the world to like,' he agreed, relieved.

'You can say that again,' Gillian declared with feeling. 'He's bigoted, big-headed and bloody-minded!' She pushed through the swing door of the staff entrance. 'Robin, I must rush,' she said hastily, catching Mary Kenny's eye as the administrator emerged from her office. 'But we must get together for a really long talk. There's so much I want to know and so much I want to tell you! Can I ring you?'

'Of course you can. I'm in the phone book,' he told her, smiling,

A sudden thought struck her. She paused on the point of hurrying away. 'Will your wife answer?' she asked, half-laughing, half-anxious. 'I don't even know if you're married these days!'

Robin gripped her shoulder with bruising fingers. 'There was only one girl that I ever wanted to marry . . .' He was tense, looking down at her with his heart in his eyes. 'Nothing's changed for me, Gillian.'

Her own heart fluttered uncertainly. 'Oh, Robin . . .'

'I mean it,' he said stoutly.

'Yes . . . yes, I know you do.' She smiled at him warmly, very moved. 'I've missed you, Robin.' It was impulsive, from the heart. She was flooded with memories of the good times they had known in those early days at Kit's. What good friends they had been and how fond they had been of each other—and how sad she had been that it had all been lost because his affection had turned into one-sided loving. 'It's really wonderful to see you again,' she added, meaning it.

Heart racing, she left him with that fervent half-promise for the future. Perhaps the future did hold all that he had hoped and apparently still hoped for despite the years. Perhaps he was an important part of the destiny that had guided her steps to Greenvale.

Perhaps he *was* her destiny . . .

CHAPTER SIX

It wasn't easy for Gillian to keep her mind on her work. Her thoughts kept turning to Robin and past days at Kit's and the might-have-been, and she found herself inclined to day-dream about the future instead of concentrating on the routine tasks and the many demands of the patients.

Mrs Maddox seemed to be more concerned about Gillian's health than her own. That stupid faint was being talked about by everyone, she discovered to her dismay. But she was. touched that the jolly, kindly woman had taken such a liking to her that she was genuinely anxious. Gillian explained about her recent illness and the move from London and the excitement and tensions of starting a new job in a new town for what seemed the umpteenth time and managed to convince her patient that she was perfectly well.

Mrs Maddox was making good progress and she was encouraged to get out of bed and take a few of the first steps towards complete recovery. Like every patient after an abdominal operation, she was nervous and apprehensive but Gillian was reassuring, imparting confidence, and full of praise as she helped the big woman into a chair.

There was a new patient in the adjoining room. Beverley Jakes was a very attractive young woman who had come in for a minor gynaecological operation. Gillian was rather amused by the see-through nightgown and négligé of apricot chiffon and the careful make-up with which she prepared for the surgeon's visit that morning.

She was busy in the room, removing all the traces of that preparation from wash-basin and dressing-table, when Mark arrived to make a brief examination of his patient in readiness for surgery on the following day.

Beverley blossomed at his entrance, casting aside her magazine and greeting him like a very dear friend with hands outstretched and cheek proffered for his kiss. 'Darling : . .' she said warmly, confidently.

'How are you?' He pressed her fingers briefly and didn't seem to notice her tilted, expectant face.

She pouted prettily, shrugged. 'I feel a fraud. I suppose I really must have this beastly operation?'

'That's entirely up to you,' he returned indifferently. 'I can only advise it.'

'Oh, if you think so . . . you know that I trust you utterly,' she declared extravagantly. 'I'm prepared to put my life in your hands!'

His smile was dry. 'It's a very minor operation, Beverley. You'll be out of here in a few days.'

'I don't want to rush things,' she said firmly. 'I want to be quite, quite well before I go home.' She paused delicately. 'You will keep a very careful eye on me, won't you, Mark?' It was low, coaxing, faintly provocative. She lay back against the mound of pillows, the chiffon falling away from the lovely curves of her breasts, smiling at him with unmistakable allure.

Mark held out a hand for the chart. Gillian passed it to him automatically. 'You shall have the best nursing care we can provide,' he drawled, very smooth. 'For instance, Nurse Grant was trained at St Christopher's—

and I shouldn't think you'd find a better nurse anywhere in the world.'

Gillian glanced at him with a sceptical gleam in her dark blue eyes. He looked back at her coolly as he returned the chart without comment. It hadn't been meant as a compliment, she thought. They were just empty words for the patient's benefit. They might even have held a touch of mockery—for *her* benefit.

At a nod, she hurried for the prepared trolley that she had left in the clinical room until it was required, carefully leaving the door open to protect his reputation. She returned very quickly to find him sitting on the side of the bed, chatting to his patient in a very relaxed manner. Beverley was openly flirting with him.

Gillian chaperoned while he carried out his examination. She suspected that the girl would have liked to be alone with the surgeon but he was strictly observing the code by ensuring the presence of a nurse in the room. Gillian thought he was wise. She guessed that Beverley Jakes was just the type to take advantage of an indiscretion.

She realised that they weren't just surgeon and patient. They knew each other socially. Like too many other women, in Gillian's opinion, the girl obviously fancied Mark Barlow and she meant to make the most of her opportunities.

They seemed to be on very easy terms. Beverley teased him and flattered him and played up to him with such obvious coquetry that Gillian was sickened. No wonder he was so spoiled, so arrogant, so carelessly contemptuous of all women, she thought crossly, hovering dutifully and obeying instructions like the well-trained nurse she was.

It was difficult to know if he found the girl attractive or merely amusing. She just didn't know enough about him. She couldn't believe that he was a womaniser although she didn't doubt his sensuality. He didn't seem to have a very high opinion of women in general. Having seen him with Louise Penistone, she felt that he might make an effort to charm for his own ends. She didn't think it came naturally to him.

He was just about to leave with a final word of reassurance, when a confident knock was followed by the opening of the door and a light voice that Gillian instantly recognised said easily: 'May I come in . . . ?'

It was Louise, looking not only beautiful but expensively elegant in a cream silk suit with a matching trifle of a hat. She laid an enormous bouquet on the bed and kissed the air in the vague direction of Beverley's cheek. She smiled at Mark with the self-possessed and slightly proprietorial warmth that Gillian had observed on the previous occasion.

'How lovely!' Beverley enthused without so much as a glance for the flowers, busily observing Mark's reaction to the arrival of her lovely friend. There was some speculation about the couple in the town and she was anxious to know if it had any foundation in fact. Louise had walked off with too many of the men she would have liked for herself. It would be too much if she had already whisked Mark Barlow out of her reach, too. 'Thank you, darling—and how sweet of you to come!'

'Of course I came. I'm concerned about you,' Louise said lightly.

'What a reflection on Mark!' Beverley declared in light-hearted reproach. 'I'm sure that a girl couldn't be in better hands!'

The look she sent the surgeon as she spoke was a provocative challenge, charged with sexuality. Noticing, Gillian replaced the chart on its hook at the bottom of the bed with a faint clatter of disapproval. A smile lurked briefly in Mark's eyes as he glanced in her direction.

'Oh, Mark knows very well that I admire him tremendously,' Louise said, smiling, and there was a great deal of meaning behind the apparently casual words.

He smiled and inclined his dark head in cool acceptance of the compliment. Gillian was instantly infuriated by that arrogant air. Perhaps he *was* a brilliant surgeon and a wow with the women but he didn't have to preen himself like a bloody peacock, she thought contemptuously, trundling the trolley towards the door.

The atmosphere was heavy with feminine lures. Feeling very unfeminine in her practical uniform dress and flat-heeled brogues, pale hair severely knotted at the nape of her neck and face bare of any make-up, Gillian was glad to escape. Both women seemed so spoiled, shallow and superficial, that she wondered what any man could find to like or admire in either of them. And it wasn't sour grapes, she thought with a flicker of pride, for she wouldn't want Mark Barlow if he was served up on a salver with an apple in his mouth. An appropriate fate for such a male chauvinist pig!

Penny met her in the corridor and glanced at her curiously. 'Feeling all right, Gillian? You look rather flushed.'

She was immediately on the defensive. 'It's a warm day. Don't look so anxious. I'm not going to faint. I don't make a habit of it!'

Penny was an easy-going girl or she might have resented the sharp retort. Instead, she shrugged. 'Well, take things easy. This isn't *Emergency Ward Ten* and you don't have to rush around being efficient. Even if you *are* a Kit's nurse.' She was teasing and there wasn't an ounce of malice behind the words. She was too good-natured.

Gillian knew she was being over-sensitive and rather silly but she couldn't muster a smile. She seemed to have lost her sense of humour since coming to Greenvale. She began to walk on towards the clinical room with the trolley.

Penny glanced along the corridor. Mark Barlow had emerged from a patient's room and was looking towards them with a slightly raised eyebrow. She misinterpreted his attitude.

She checked Gillian with a hand on her arm. 'Mr Barlow is waiting for assistance,' she said quickly, whisking the trolley out of her hands. 'I'll take this. Go and see what he wants.'

Gillian turned and retraced her steps, rather reluctantly, too conscious of his steady but indifferent scrutiny as he waited for her to reach him. It was typical of the man that he wouldn't take even one step towards her, she thought with impatience—he was so damnably sure of himself!

Joining him, her chin tilted unconsciously. 'Do you want me?' she asked, not very graciously, and immediately regretted the unfortunate choice of words. The grey eyes narrowed and raked her slight figure as though he was carefully considering a very different kind of offer. The colour stormed into her face and her eyes sparked an angry rebuke despite the hint of humour in his expression.

'I'm hoping that you may prove to be useful—as a nurse,' he drawled with a momentary, slightly mischievous hesitation. 'As you know, I shall be operating tomorrow. Miss Jakes is on my list, of course. Also a gall-bladder removal and a rather tricky hernioplasty. I imagine you are familiar with the procedures and I would like you to assist me. My regular theatre nurse is leaving at the end of the month to work in New Zealand and I shall need a replacement. It's possible that you'll be suitable.'

Gillian's face immediately brightened and she promptly forgot her indignation. She knew she was a good theatre nurse and she couldn't help feeling that her talents were wasted on routine nursing.

'If my work was good enough to suit Sir Geoffrey or Paul Ritchie or Peter Lincoln then I don't think you'll have any cause for complaint,' she said confidently.

Mark regarded her thoughtfully. 'Heaven forbid that I should consider myself superior in any way to such eminent men,' he said, very dry. 'I daresay your work is excellent. It's your attitude that may cause a few problems, I feel."

Gillian stiffened. 'My attitude?'

'You know as well as I do that a certain rapport must exist between surgeon and nurse for them to be able to work together as a successful team,' he reminded her bluntly.

She did know it. It was very important. They needed to be so attuned that they thought and worked as one during an operation. She needed to anticipate his every requirement, it was not enough to be familiar with procedure or surgical techniques. A good theatre nurse was a surgeon's right hand. He had to be able to rely on her—and there was no room for mutual dislike in an operating theatre.

But she was proud and she couldn't pretend to like him even to get a job that she particularly wanted. She knew that she could never work with him and enjoy it.

'I'm sorry,' she said stiffly. 'But I'm not a member of the Mark Barlow Admiration Society, I'm afraid. And I never will be!'

Mark's mouth hardened abruptly. Damn the girl! He had given her more than enough chances to bury the hatchet—and every time she insisted on planting it firmly between his shoulder-blades! He turned on his heel and walked away, too angry to continue the conversation with an obstinate and very silly young woman.

Gillian looked after him, her heart sinking. Her pride and her impulsive tongue had cost her the one thing she really wanted, she realised. What did she think she gained by continually clashing with a man like Mark Barlow? He held all the aces, after all.

Steve came to see Beverley Jakes later that morning. As the anaesthetist responsible for her safety while she was on the operating table, he needed to make his own check on her heart and lungs and ask certain relevant questions.

Gillian was with a patient when she saw him pass the door. She hoped there would be an opportunity for a few words before he went away.

Steve made the opportunity. She was in the spacious and well-appointed ward kitchen preparing a milk feed for her patient, when he came into the room.

'I'd love a coffee,' he said, smiling. 'What are my chances?'

Gillian glanced over her shoulder, a smile in her own

eyes. 'I'll make some in a moment.'

'Good girl!' he dropped a kiss on the back of her neck as she busied herself with mixing the feed.

'Don't ask if I'm all right or I shall probably scream,' Gillian said quickly, very light.

He laughed. 'People getting on your nerves, love?'

She smiled wryly. 'Oh, I know I should be touched that people are so kind—and I am, of course. After all, I'm a newcomer and it's surprising that so many people I don't even know have stopped to ask how I am!'

'We don't get a lot of excitement,' Steve said, eyes twinkling. 'And it isn't every day that Mark Barlow rushes to the rescue of a damsel in distress. He's much more likely to step over an unconscious nurse in his path than scoop her into his arms, give her the kiss of life and then ride off with her on his dashing white charger.'

Gillian's laughing eyes held a hint of reproach as she turned to him. 'It sounds very romantic. But it didn't happen!'

'He didn't pick you up from the floor?'

'Well, yes, I believe he did do that . . .'

'No kiss of life?' His blue eyes danced with mischief.

'No! It was Penny who looked after me, in fact, she brought me round!'

'And he didn't whisk you home by the modern-day equivalent of an Arab steed?'

She smiled reluctantly. 'Well, yes—but I do hope that people aren't making too much of the whole thing,' she said firmly.

'It won't even be a nine-day wonder,' he said comfortingly. 'He's announcing his engagement to Louise Penistone next week.'

It wasn't unexpected. It wasn't even of interest. But

Gillian felt an odd little pang of foolish disappointment that after all she would never know just how it felt to have his arms about her and that dark head very close to her own.

She shook off the thought, irritated by its absurdity. 'Louise Penistone?' she echoed, playing for time.

'Hugh Penistone is her father.' He looked at her curiously. 'You must have had a potted history of the clinic from Mary Kenny at your interview. He's the man who founded Greenvale. Louise is his only child. A beautiful girl, too. Mark's no fool,' he said dryly. 'There's a lot of men who'd like to be in his shoes.'

Gillian carried the milk feed carefully to the door, finding that she was glad of an excuse to leave him for a few moments and hoping that the subject of Mark Barlow's engagement would not be renewed on her return.

'I'll be back to make your coffee,' she told him with careful nonchalance. 'Two minutes . . .'

She was a little longer, in fact. By the time she returned, Steve was setting out cups and spooning coffee into them, and the kettle was coming to the boil.

'You are house-trained,' she said warmly.

He grinned. 'I can do card tricks, too.'

Over coffee, to avoid any further mention of Mark Barlow and his personal affairs, Gillian spoke of her meeting with an old friend. She wasn't surprised to learn that Steve was acquainted with Robin. In a small community, it was inevitable that members of the same profession would know each other, belong to the same clubs, move in the same social circles.

They frequently played golf together and Steve often dined with Robin and his uncle. For the first time,

Gillian learned that there was a cousin who ran the house and looked after the two doctors and she was quick to catch a certain note in Steve's voice when he referred to the girl called Diantha. There had obviously been some kind of an affair, she thought shrewdly. When he too casually remarked that it was some time since he had been to the house, Gillian knew that it was over and that he was feeling uncomfortable and perhaps guilty about it.

He was very open about his liking for women. She didn't doubt that he was a light-hearted but harmless flirt. Nor did she doubt that women found it easy to fall in love with the attractive, personable and warm-hearted anaesthetist. In a very short time she had become fond of him and felt at ease with him. They were friends. She knew that they would never be anything more. She hoped that he realised it, too.

She hadn't meant to talk about Mark Barlow at all. But suddenly she found herself telling Steve that the surgeon had virtually offered her the job as his theatre nurse and that she had refused.

Steve was thoughtful. 'You sound regretful.'

Gillian gave a rueful nod. 'I am. I'd have loved the job,' she admitted frankly.

'Then why didn't you leap at it?'

She hesitated. 'It's hard to explain . . .'

'No, it isn't. You don't like each other and think it will affect your working relationship,' he said shrewdly.

She smiled. 'Something like that.'

Steve shrugged. 'We all have colleagues that we can't stand, Gillian. The profession's crowded with bossy nurses and bumptious doctors and surgeons who think themselves a cut above the rest of the world. Greenvale has fewer than most, fortunately—and I get on pretty well with most people. Mark can be very difficult, I know. He isn't the best-loved man in the district, by any means. But he is a very good surgeon. He needs a good theatre nurse—and you came with glowing references. He had you earmarked to replace Helen Irving as soon as he heard about you. I wish you could have heard him enthusing about Greenvale's good luck to get a Kit's nurse with considerable theatre experience.'

Gillian stared. 'You're joking!'

'No, I'm not. The job was yours after the first interview, love. Didn't anyone tell you?'

She shook her head. 'I answered the ad for a surgical nurse. There was a vague reference to theatre work but I might have prompted that by asking if there was any likelihood of it.' She was beginning to be angry. 'And he played it so cool! Making me feel that it was a rare privilege to have the opportunity of the job, when he'd been rubbing his hands with glee at the thought of working with me! Really looking forward to it, I daresay—and then implying that he doubted if I'd be good enough but he was magnanimously prepared to give me a trial!' The flush of fury was surging into her small face and her eyes were starting to sparkle with militant indignation.

Steve grinned. 'That sounds just like our Mark,' he said lightly, amused. 'Stiff-necked as ever!' He glanced at his watch and rose to his feet, pushing away his empty coffee cup. 'He's the type who'd lose out on something he dearly wanted rather than admit to wanting it at all. Pride! He's top-heavy with it.' He moved to the door. 'Me . . . I'm not proud, love. You're the nicest thing that's happened in a long time—and I don't hesitate to say so!' He blew her a kiss and vanished, leaving the memory of his cheerful grin behind him, like the Cheshire Cat in *Alice in Wonderland*.

Gillian rinsed the cups, fuming. She would dearly love to bounce Mark Barlow to Land's End and back, she thought bitterly. He was the most arrogant, the most insufferable, the most detestable man she had ever known. How could he adopt such a supercilious attitude towards her when he had apparently been as pleased as punch to learn that she was joining the staff of Greenvale! Having Kit's in common, sharing a keen interest in surgery, they ought to be friends. Instead, a rampant hostility had existed between them from the very first moment of meeting.

Leaving the clinic that afternoon after the day's work, she saw Mark talking to Mary Kenny in the grounds. She hesitated and then hurried across to join them with one of her sweetest smiles.

'Mr Barlow! I'm so glad that I caught you before you left,' she declared brightly and with a convincing air of humility. 'I've been thinking it over and I would like to assist tomorrow if the offer still stands—I do hope you'll feel that I'm good enough to be your theatre nurse when Miss Irving leaves.'

Mary Kenny looked from one to the other, puzzled. 'But that's all settled, isn't it?' she said uncertainly.

Gillian was pleased to notice that the surgeon was slightly disconcerted. 'I'd love to do the job but Mr Barlow feels that he doesn't know enough about my work to be sure that I'm suitable,' she said innocently.

The administrator laughed gently. 'Oh, my dear! You must have misunderstood him. We know all about your excellent record as a theatre sister at St Christopher's!

Why, Sir Geoffrey wrote a personal letter to say how sorry he had been to lose you and what an asset you would be to Greenvale.'

Gillian looked directly at Mark with a challenge in her dark blue eyes. 'That was kind but just what I'd expect from him. He was always very charming to me and extremely courteous on all occasions. A great man, loved and respected by everyone. There aren't enough like him!'

It was almost an accusation. Mark smiled slightly. 'Every surgeon has his own methods. I'm more likely to criticise than charm you with smiles and compliments. But if I say that you've done a good job and I'm pleased, you'll know that I mean it. My praise is hard-earned, Gillian. It's up to you to decide if you want to work for it. I hope that you will.' He turned to the older woman. 'Mary, I'll ring you this evening after I've talked to Louise and Hugh. They might decide to keep it as a very private occasion.'

With those words he was gone, walking towards the car park. Gillian said goodnight and followed more slowly, swinging her bag. His parting words seemed to confirm Steve's claim that his engagement was soon to be announced. There would probably be a few shattered hopes and dreams when it was known that he meant to marry Louise Penistone, she thought dryly, thankful that his undeniable good looks and physical magnetism didn't encourage *her* to waste her dreams on a cold-blooded man like Mark Barlow . . .

CHAPTER SEVEN

THE evening was wet and windy and Gillian could have found plenty in the flat to occupy the rather lonely hours. But she felt the need to go out for a while. She had a lot on her mind and she wanted to think it out. And, as always, her mind turned to the sea with its ability to calm and soothe her turbulent thoughts and emotions.

She put on jeans and a sweater and a thin anorak, for the evening was rather chilly although it was late summer. She took the Mini and drove the short distance over the downs to the coast, avoiding the resort that was so popular with holiday-makers and day-trippers. She found a quiet section of the shore, parked the car and began to walk, hands thrust into her pockets and face lifted against the elements.

She seemed to be the only one out on that bleak, rather wild evening and she preferred it that way. In the far distance, a man walked his dog but she scarcely noticed him. The spray from the rough water flicked her face, so close did she walk to the edge of the shore, small feet in sensible brogues leaving their imprints in the damp sand.

Deep in thought, Gillian walked slowly and steadily along the beach, pale hair whipped by the breeze and face glowing from the chilly spray.

So much had happened in a few days that her thoughts and emotions were in a whirl. Coming to Greenvale, meeting Steve, clashing with Mark Barlow, finding Robin again so unexpectedly. A trio of doctors had invaded her life—and each one seemed to have something to contribute to it, she felt.

Steve was a dear, already a good friend, promising to bring a lot of fun and laughter into her life. Robin was a very important part of her past who might turn out to be all of her future, she thought with a lift of her heart. Mark was someone with whom she had to come to terms if they were to work in close proximity for the year she expected to spend at Greenvale—and he threatened to be a problem.

Steve liked and admired her with the impulsive giving of affection that was obviously very much in character for him. Robin was still in love with her and he had a very special place in her heart. Mark disliked her as much as she disliked him but there was a kind of challenge in their hostility that was stimulating—and even exciting at times, she confessed, striving to be utterly honest with herself.

He was exciting in a way that Steve could never be and in a way that Robin never had been for all the warmth of her affection for him. But there was a certain danger in that excitement, Gillian realised. She wondered if it stirred his blood, too. There was a sensuality about the surgeon that triggered a shafting flame in her body. It was a matter of chemistry but surely it needed a mutual spark?

A trio of doctors, she mused again. She liked Steve. She felt that she might love Robin more than she had known. And she wanted Mark Barlow with a passionate intensity of physical longing that was frightening, because they would be thrown together again and again—

and it would never do for him to become aware of the desire he kindled without even trying.

The man in the distance turned and began to walk towards her, whistling his dog to heel. Gillian was unaware of him, hearing only the sea in her ears and a very disturbing dream of a virtual stranger blinding her eyes to reality.

Mark had almost drawn level before she looked at him with seeing eyes. She came to an abrupt, startled halt.

He had recognised her some moments before. His attention was caught and held by the long, pale hair that the wind whipped about her face and by something familiar about the slight figure in jeans and anorak that battled against the elements on that bleak shore.

'Hallo,' Gillian said uncertainly, not knowing what else to say to a man who seemed to have been conjured out of thin air by her thoughts of him. Every nerve in her body had begun to tingle as she recognised the identity of the tall man with his proud, dark good looks and lithe build.

'Out in this wild weather?' he challenged lightly.

Gillian thrust her hands deeper into her pockets to prevent herself from foolishly reaching out to touch him to discover if it was really him or just a figment of her imagination.

'I like to walk and I needed to think something out,' she said, rather defensively.

'Do you want me to pretend that I haven't seen you?' There was unexpected understanding in the deep, rather lazy drawl.

A smile trembled briefly on Gillian's lips. She looked at the surgeon, noting that his dark hair glistened wetly from the rain and that the shoulders of his tweed jacket were quite damp. In casual clothes and with rumpled curls, he looked younger, less forbidding, almost human . . . and attractive enough to threaten a less level head than her own.

'What about you?' she asked on a sudden impulse, challenging in her turn. 'I didn't expect you to like this sort of thing.'

'Henry does.' He indicated the black labrador who was dashing in and out of the water, barking madly at the wild waves. 'He insisted on bringing me here this evening. It's one of his favourite places,' he told her, eyes twinkling with a little humour. He saw that the light words brought the flickering smile into full radiance, illuminating her small face with a sudden and rather enchanting warmth. He had known that she was a pretty girl, he now discovered that she could be very lovely.

'And you fell in with his wishes? It seems unlikely,' Gillian said dryly.

As she turned to walk back along the beach, unconsciously guided by the fact that he had been walking in that direction, he fell into step by her side.

'Oh, I didn't mind,' he said, very light. 'This reduces me to a man, after all.' He gestured at the sea, the rolling horizon, the fast-approaching bank of black cloud that heralded the night. 'At times I'm encouraged to believe that I'm a superior being. Out here, minimised by the elements, I realise how unimportant I am in the scheme of things.'

Gillian liked the glimpse of humour in him. She liked a man who could laugh at himself and encourage others to laugh with him, too. Suddenly, for the first time and quite unexpectedly, she felt that it might even be possible to like this man . . .

They walked on in silence, wind and rain in their faces. The light was fading fast and she suddenly stumbled over a clump of stones in the sand. His hand sped automatically to her elbow. Gillian smiled her thanks, knowing that her whole being had rocked at his touch.

Physical attraction, she knew. It sent a kind of shock quivering down her spine, heightening all her awareness of the man by her side. But she hadn't known that it could be so forceful that she would feel like throwing all caution to the wind that blew so strongly along the shore.

His hand slid down her arm to capture her fingers. She looked up at him quickly. He looked back at her with a quizzical lift of an eyebrow. She knew she ought to snatch her hand away. Instead, she allowed it to lie in his firm clasp, tingling, wondering if he was aware of his effect on her senses.

The steady drizzle turned abruptly to a fierce squall of rain. 'Come on!' he said urgently and they began to run towards a wooden shelter that was close to the spot where she had parked the Mini. The dog raced at their heels, barking furiously, eager to join in a new game.

Gillian was breathless and laughing and a little trembly by the time they reached the sanctuary of the shelter. She leaned against the wall, her heart pounding.

Mark looked down at her with some concern, recalling that she had recently been ill, remembering that she had fainted and how slight and frail she had seemed when he lifted her in his arms. She didn't seem to be very strong. He wondered how she was going to cope with the demands and the tensions of the operating theatre. It would be made all the more difficult if she was still so determined not to like him or accept him as a friend.

'All right?' he asked, a little abruptly.

Gillian nodded. 'Out of condition,' she said, half laughing.

He brushed the fine hair from her wet face with both hands and felt her quiver at his touch. Swift surprise glimmered in his grey eyes. He saw a touching hint of defensiveness in her expression and knew its cause with the sudden insight of experience. His body stirred with its own awareness of a sexual chemistry that defied logic —or liking. His hands moved slowly to cradle her fair head in a kind of caress. Her eyes widened. He drew her towards him with intent.

They stood very close and his mouth hovered just above her own. Gillian could sense the throb of desire in his taut, lean body. She waited for him to kiss her, heart hammering. She would be angry with him later. Just now, she was melting with a longing that was alarming in its intensity.

Mark let her go, abruptly. It had always been his maxim to avoid any kind of relationship with the nurses he met in the course of his work. It led to complications that a dedicated and ambitious doctor just didn't need. He might be very tempted to make love to this pretty girl who had quickened his senses so unexpectedly, but he had learned at an early age to master his sensuality. He knew the danger of giving way to desire without a thought for the consequences. A kiss or two might seem to be harmless enough, but he realised that it wouldn't stop at that. For their mutual wanting was too fierce a flame, swiftly ignited.

Gillian knew that he had fought temptation—and won. Like herself, he realised that it was just a fleeting physical excitement, without rhyme or reason, that mustn't be allowed a free rein. For her, there was Robin

A Sensational Offer from largest publishe

JOIN OUR READER
TAKE TWO BOOKS

Every month we publish twelve brand new Romances – wonderful books by the world's biggest names in romantic fiction – letting you escape into a world of fascinating relationships, exotic locations and heart-stopping excitement. Thousands of readers worldwide already find that Mills & Boon Romances have them spellbound from the very first page to the last loving embrace.

And now, by becoming a member of the Mills & Boon Reader Service for just one year, you can receive *all twelve* books hot off the presses each month – *but you only pay for ten.*

That's right – *two books free every month for twelve months.* And as a member of the Reader

Service, your monthly parcel of books will be delivered direct to your door, postage and packing free. And just look at these other exclusive benefits:

THE NEWEST ROMANCES – reserved the printers for you each month and delivered direct to your door by Mills & Boon.

POSTAGE AND PACKING FREE – unli other book clubs, we pay all the extras. You only pay the same as you would in the shops.

14 DAY FREE TRIAL PERIOD – you ca return your first parcel of books within fortnight and owe nothing.

Mills & Boon – the World's
of Romantic Fiction.

SERVICE AND
FREE EVERY MONTH!

- **FREE MONTHLY NEWSLETTER** – keeps you up-to-date with new books and book bargains.
- **SPECIAL OFFERS**, recipes, patterns and competitions. This year our lucky winners are spending a fortnight in Barbados.
- **EXCLUSIVE BARGAIN BOOK OFFERS** – available only to subscribers.
- **HELPFUL, FRIENDLY SERVICE** from the girls at Mills & Boon. You can ring us any time on 01-684 2141.

u have nothing to lose, and a whole
ew world of romance to gain. Just fill in and
st the coupon today.

Mills & Boon Reader Service,
PO Box 236,
Croydon,
Surrey CR9 3RU.

For you from Mills & Boon:

* The very latest titles delivered hot from the presses to your door each month; postage and packing free.

* FREE monthly newsletter.

A parcel of brand new romances – delivere direct to your door every month.

Simply fill in your name and address on the FREE BOOKS Certificate overleaf and post it today. You don't need a stamp. We will then send you the TWELVE latest Mills & Boon Romances – but you only pay for TEN.

That's *two books Free* – every month!

to consider—and for him, there was the beautiful girl that he was planning to marry. It would be much too easy to forget them and everything else in each other's arms, but it could only be a short-lived and much-regretted ecstasy. For they didn't really like each other at all.

Yet, woman-like, she was piqued that he hadn't kissed her when she had been in the mood to respond. She moved away from him, hoping that he wouldn't suspect how much she had wanted that whisked-away kiss.

The big dog launched himself on her with heavy paws, tail wagging with the offer of friendship. Speaking eyes begged for attention and he uttered a short, eager bark.

Gillian was glad of the distraction. She rubbed Henry's silky ears and murmured dog-talk to him, carefully not looking at Mark, thankful that the turmoil of her senses was beginning to quieten. He leaned against the wooden frame of the shelter, staring out to sea.

She wondered what had happened to his plans. He had spoken to Mary Kenny as if he was expecting to spend the evening with the Penistones. Yet he was here with his dog on a deserted beach on a squally evening, some miles from the town. She marvelled at the odd chance that had brought them both to the same place at the same time.

She wished she could feel that the brief encounter had improved their relationship. But that almost-kiss had been humiliating rather than flattering and she was a little angry. Perhaps it was just as well that she had no reason to like him any better. They needed to keep a certain distance between them or they might both be consumed by a dangerous flame . . .

'It's getting late,' she said, straightening and brushing the marks of muddy paws from her jeans.

He held his watch to the fading light. 'Nearly nine o'clock.'

'I want to get back before it's really dark. I'm not too sure of the road. The rain's easing off now, I think.' She gave Henry a last caress and allowed Mark a cool smile that didn't hint at her lingering chagrin because he hadn't kissed her, after all. 'I'll see you in the morning. Complete with gown and mask!'

'Looking forward to it?'

She hesitated. 'I'm a little nervous,' she confessed. 'I shall be working with a temperamental surgeon who doesn't make allowances, I'm told.'

He didn't react to the tentative olive branch. 'Where's your car?'

'Over there.' Gillian gestured in the vague direction of the parked Mini, refusing to admit to disappointment let alone show it. 'By the pub . . .'

'So's mine.' He swung into step by her side, matching his long strides to her slower pace, the dog trotting at their heels.

He didn't reach for her hand this time. Gillian wondered if he had decided that it was safer for them to be enemies than try for any degree of friendship.

The Mercedes was parked a short distance from her Mini. It must have been there when she drove up, Gillian realised. But she hadn't noticed. She wouldn't have connected the sleek silver car with the surgeon, anyway. Who would have thought that Mark Barlow shared her liking for evening walks on a sea shore whatever the weather?

They paused when they reached her car.

Gillian fingered the car keys in her anorak pocket, feeling she ought to wish him a casual goodnight and drive away, but finding it oddly difficult to bring a chance encounter to an end. She wasn't at ease with him but she didn't want to part with him. Her thoughts and emotions were foolishly muddled, in fact.

'I'm not surprised you were so ill if you take such little care of yourself,' he said abruptly, flicking her damp hair with an impatient hand. 'You're running the risk of another bout of pneumonia. You look quite chilled. Come over to the pub and I'll get you a brandy. I could use one myself.'

He took her arm and swept her across the road before she could protest that she didn't like brandy and she didn't want to linger in a pub with a man she didn't really want to know. So she said nothing and he took her silence for consent.

The pub was almost empty. It was the kind of evening when few people had ventured out. A fire burned cheerfully in the hearth and Mark steered her towards it. He settled her on a padded bench and went to the bar for drinks. Henry flumped to the floor and put his head on her foot and sighed happily, his wet coat already steaming in the warmth from the fire.

Mark wrinkled his nose when he came back with the brandies. 'You're smelling like a dog, Henry,' he scolded, stirring the labrador with his foot. Henry grunted, shifted his position slightly and went back to sleep.

Gillian hid her smile in her brandy glass. Not liking him, not feeling kindly disposed to him at that particular moment, she didn't see why she should admit to being amused by the conversation between a man and his dog.

Mark leaned towards her, elbows resting on his knees, brandy glass rotating slowly in his muscular, long-fingered, surgeon's hands. 'Henry's taken a fancy to you,' he drawled.

'He's very discerning,' she retorted. She smiled sweetly. 'Which is more than I can say for his owner!' She couldn't resist the barb.

He shrugged. 'You don't need me to fancy you,' he said bluntly. 'You've had Steve running round in circles ever since you arrived at Greenvale—and I gather that McAllister's had a thing about you for years. He couldn't talk of anything else but you this morning. I eventually had to remind him that we'd met to discuss a patient and not the love of his life.'

Gillian felt the heat steal into her face at the slightly sardonic words. 'We haven't met in a long time,' she said defensively.

'I believe he's hoping to make up for lost time. So I was rather surprised to find you out on your own this evening. Couldn't you choose between the pair of them?'

She didn't answer. She sipped her brandy carefully, disliking the taste but welcoming the warming glow. She realised that she *had* been chilled by the wind and the rain.

She could sense his gaze, the considering grey eyes intent on her face. She could sense the hint of mockery in the smile that probably hovered about his sensual mouth. She wondered if he thought that she meant to play one man off against the other. He must have formed a very poor opinion of her, she thought, needled.

For some moments, she wouldn't look at him. She wondered how she came to be in a pub with him at all. She wondered why she had stopped to speak to him on the beach. She wondered why she couldn't stop wondering about him.

She raised her eyes reluctantly and found that he was regarding her, unsmiling. She looked back at him with dislike, all her hackles rising. How could she warm to a man who gave nothing of himself to anyone and seemed to expect too much from everyone else, particularly women!

He was a detestable man and she marvelled that she had been so weak with wanting at his touch. Well, he wouldn't get the chance to touch her again—ever.

She leaped to her feet, impatient. Henry yelped mournfully as she trod on a paw. She looked down at the dog, swiftly contrite.

Mark smiled slightly. 'Tread softly for you tread on poor Henry's dreams,' he drawled, misquoting Yeats.

Gillian met his eyes and found them warm with unexpected laughter. She hesitated, uncertain. He was laughing at her again but for once it wasn't unkind, she decided. She smiled reluctantly and stooped to apologise to Henry with a pat. He thumped his tail to show that she was forgiven and yawned widely.

'Where were you going, anyway?' Mark asked carelessly. 'You haven't finished your drink.'

'I *am* going home,' she said firmly and left him, making resolutely for the door.

He drained the last of his own brandy then rose and followed her leisurely from the pub, calling Henry to heel.

Gillian was in the process of opening her car door when he walked towards her and said her name so peremptorily that she turned, bridling. 'What is it?'

He reached her.

She looked up at him, suddenly wary.

'I do fancy you,' he said quietly. Then he bent his dark head and kissed her in the rain.

She had been kissed before, many times, and had found it enjoyable if not as exciting as she had been led to expect. Being kissed by Mark Barlow was an entirely new experience.

She hadn't known that her heart would stop, that the world would spin and there would be so much intoxication in a mere kiss. She hadn't known that his lips would be sweet as well as warm, touched with a magic that tugged at her senses and invited her to drown in the enchantment of his arms. She hadn't known that she would feel as if she was suddenly and gloriously alive for the first time in her life, athrob in every fibre of her being and eager to know more of a promised paradise.

Her lips clung, reluctant for the magic to end. It was suddenly the most important thing in the world that he should be caught up in that same magic. She wanted the moment to be as memorable for him as it certainly would be for her. She wanted it to be a new beginning. She didn't even dare to think how it might end . . .

Mark was shaken. For him, it had been an impulsive yielding to sudden temptation, that vein of dark mischief in his make-up. She was a pretty girl and he had wondered if she would react with her usual rebellious spirit if he kissed her. He hadn't expected the melting sweetness of her response. He hadn't expected the fire to leap in his loins with such compelling urgency. He hadn't expected to feel that there was only one way to end an evening that had begun without even the thought of her.

She drew away, trembling.

Mark didn't doubt that she was consumed by the same flame as himself. He didn't doubt that she knew what she was doing when she welcomed and returned his kiss and leaned her body against him. He didn't doubt that she was as sexually experienced as most of the women in his life.

'Where do we go from here?' he asked abruptly. 'Your place or mine?'

The directness of his approach shocked Gillian back to reality. Did he think he had only to kiss her and she would be ready to leap into bed with him? She was suddenly angry . . . and all the more indignant because it was so nearly true!

'I know where I'm going,' she said coldly, thrusting past him. 'You can go to hell!' She scrambled into the driving seat and slotted in the ignition key and the little Mini's tyres almost scorched the road as it took off for home, leaving him looking after her with a wry expression.

All the way home, Gillian chided herself for allowing him to get close enough to kiss her—and for allowing him to realise her response to that kiss. She had kissed him back like any naive schoolgirl on her first date. She had encouraged him to think that she was an easy conquest. She was a fool!

She ought to have passed him on the beach without a word, she scolded herself. She didn't even like him, after all. She hadn't wanted to be involved in any way with a man like Mark Barlow.

She shouldn't have allowed him to walk along with her, to talk to her, to take her hand in that familiar fashion. Anyone observing them might have believed they were lovers out for an evening stroll, too much in love to care for the inclement weather, she thought bitterly.

She shouldn't have allowed him to buy her a drink and disarm her with a smattering of the charm that apparently endeared him to too many women. A few humorous remarks, a caressing touch of his hand, a mere glimpse of the warmth that it seemed he was glad to bestow on everyone but herself—and she was ready to tumble into his arms! Gillian was furious with her weakness for a near-stranger.

Heaven knew how she was going to meet him the next morning! She might pretend that she had regarded it as a meaningless kiss, a nothing, a try-on by a sensual man who was also an opportunist. But she knew—and she had the awful feeling that Mark Barlow knew—that it had been the kind of a kiss that could change a girl's whole life.

She didn't like him.

But she felt a strong physical attraction that weakened her resolve to keep him firmly at a distance.

Most alarming of all, Gillian wondered if she was just a little in love with him . . .

CHAPTER EIGHT

THE moment that Gillian had been dreading came and went almost unnoticed. She was busy in the larger of the two theatres, scrubbed-up and green-gowned, checking the instrument trolley and mentally revising the procedure for the hernioplasty that was the first operation on the list, when Mark entered and nodded to her so impersonally that it was hard to believe that kiss had ever happened.

Before she could give the matter more than a passing thought, the patient was being wheeled in from the ante-room. Steve was busy with valves and cylinders and there was no time to think of anything but the job for which she had been trained.

She was keyed-up, determined to do well, anxious that Mark shouldn't have the slightest cause to find fault with her work. But within moments of Steve's nod and the first incision of the scalpel that she slapped into Mark's waiting hand, she relaxed and began to enjoy her involvement in his surgical skill. Assisting him proved to be a delight. It was impossible not to admire his expertise and his confidence or to realise that here was a really good surgeon who loved his work.

It was a lengthy and delicate operation, inserting a plastic mesh into the abdominal wall of a middle-aged man to reduce and repair a chronic inguinal hernia. When it was over and the patient had been wheeled away to the recovery room, Mark stripped off the thin surgical gloves and tossed them into the 'dirty' bin. He drew down his mask.

Gillian waited, apprehensive.

He looked into the slightly anxious dark blue eyes as though he was seeing her for the first time that morning. Then he nodded. 'You were good,' he said brusquely. 'Very good. Thanks.'

He walked from the theatre.

Gillian discovered that she was trembling. It had been that important to her. She knew that with one adverse word from Mark Barlow she wouldn't have worked in the theatre at Greenvale again. He could have taken his revenge for the rebuff of the previous evening. But, as Penny had claimed, he was quick but he was fair—and he wasn't a fool. She knew she was a good theatre nurse. So did he. He needed someone efficient and reliable and with her kind of experience. Personal feelings had no place in an operating theatre. No one could be more impersonal than Mark Barlow when he wished, she thought wryly. Not a word had passed between them that morning which wasn't connected with their work.

The night before she had telephoned Robin as soon as she reached the flat, determined to shake off the absurd fancy that she could lose her heart to a man like Mark Barlow. Talking to the delighted Robin, making eager plans to meet, her head and heart had returned to their usual even keel.

It had been a momentary madness, a kind of magic. The power of sexual attraction wasn't a myth, she had discovered, much to her dismay. It could transform a level-headed girl into a near wanton in a moment and it was disturbing to realise how close she had come to melting surrender. The circumstances had been against him and on her side, fortunately. Another time, another place . . .

Steve smiled at her. 'That's the first hurdle behind you, love. It wasn't so bad, was it?'

She liked his ready understanding, his warm friendliness. He was the kind of man that any girl would find easy to love, she felt. Like Robin, unlike Mark Barlow, he was uncomplicated.

'I was shaking in my shoes,' she confessed with a light laugh.

'It didn't show,' he assured her warmly. 'Mark likes confidence and you seemed to have plenty of it. I thought we made a good team.'

'Everything went well,' she pointed out, a little dryly. 'No problems. He won't feel that I've proved myself until I've coped with a crisis or two!'

'I daresay you've coped with a few crises in your time. Mark admires your work more than he's saying, believe me. He never does say much—until he's annoyed and then he says much more than he means. You'll learn to know him, Gillian. I'm not saying that you'll learn to love him, of course,' he added, eyes twinkling. 'We don't want that to happen, do we? You're reserved for me, love.'

She smiled but she felt a twinge of anxiety. She would need to be blind and deaf and stupid not to be aware of his growing affection for her, she thought ruefully. He might be light-hearted about it but it was possible that he could be hurt. She must be careful not to encourage him. For there was Robin after all—and she must make up her mind if she really wanted to resume their comfortable, undemanding relationship with its promise of eventual marriage. If she didn't, then she must be careful not to encourage him to hope, either.

She was meeting him that evening. Perhaps it would clarify the way she felt about him after so long.

And perhaps it would banish the lingering impact of another man's kiss . . .

By the end of the day's list, Gillian felt that she had acquitted herself reasonably well. But Mark didn't add any more to those first terse words of praise. At the same time, he hadn't been critical of her work.

With only three operations on the list, it had been much more leisurely than she had been used to at Kit's. There was time for the surgeon and anaesthetist to relax between each operation and plenty of time for Gillian to ensure the smooth running of the theatre and to check that everyone else was doing their job properly. She slipped easily into the rôle of theatre nurse. Used to dealing with sensitive juniors, she knew just how to organise things as she wished without alienating the rest of the theatre staff. Gillian felt that it was more important to be heeded than liked and she could be strict. But she had a warmth and a sweetness of personality that won her liking as well as respect—and she found that the Kit's badge went a long way towards her acceptance by her newly-acquired colleagues at Greenvale.

That evening, Robin smiled at her across the table and leaned over to touch her hand. 'You're beautiful,' he said simply.

Gillian smiled and shook her head at the exaggeration, knowing that she was far from beautiful. But she thought that she might be looking pretty and she was glad for his sake. It was a long time since she had dressed up for an occasion and she had taken the rose taffeta from her wardrobe with some hesitation. But Robin had said that the country club dances were formal affairs and she knew that he wanted to show her off to all his friends.

She loved the elegant lines of the frock, flattering the swell of her breasts and her small waist and slender hips. She loved its luxurious swishing of silk when she moved. She loved the soft colour that reflected in her cheeks and deepened her eyes and enhanced the fairness of hair and skin.

Wearing her hair down and curling slightly on her shoulders, pale and gleaming in the soft light, she felt pretty and feminine and alluring. She had discarded capable, competent and practical Gillian Grant, Kit's nurse, theatre nurse. She was simply Gillian, all woman, basking in the affection and admiration that glowed in Robin's eyes, warmed his voice and vibrated in his touch. She felt young and light of heart—just a little reckless.

'Let's dance,' Robin said eagerly as music filled the room and couples began to drift towards the dance floor.

Gillian rose obediently, knowing that he was longing to hold her and that dancing was the excuse he needed. He had never been shy or uncertain in the past. Now he seemed afraid of losing her again with a wrong word or an incautious act.

Dancing with him was easy and effortless. Their steps seemed to match with the timelessness of long-ago harmony. His arms held her close and he pressed his cheek to her hair. She could feel the heavy thud of his heart against her breast.

She was surrounded by the love that he still felt for her. It was warm, comforting, comfortable, making no demands on her. It didn't have to be exciting, she told

herself firmly, rejecting the critical thought that something was missing just as it had always been. Perhaps he
didn't stir her senses. But perhaps she was wrong to
suppose that sexual attraction was a vital part of any
meaningful relationship between a man and a woman.
Perhaps a woman was only meant to be awakened and
initiated into the delights of sex by the man she married.
In which case, she ought to feel quite guilty when she
recalled the quivering excitement that Mark Barlow's
nearness had aroused in her, she thought wryly.

Still thinking of the surgeon, she found herself looking
over Robin's shoulder and directly into those disconcerting grey eyes. He seemed to have a gift for turning up in
her life at such moments.

He was dancing with Louise Penistone, a vision of
loveliness in flame-coloured chiffon. He smiled at Gillian, surprising her into a slight blush. But she refused to
recognise the unexpected charm and melting warmth of
that smile. She looked back at him coolly and inclined
her head in the merest nod of acknowledgment.

She might have known he would be there to spoil her
evening, she thought bitterly, looking up at Robin and
laughing happily as he whirled her about the dance floor.

As the music stopped, Mark and his lovely girlfriend
came to a halt just a few feet away from them. Knowing
them both, Robin greeted them eagerly, demanded to
know if they were with friends and invited them to their
table for a drink.

Introduced to Louise Penistone, Gillian wasn't at all
surprised that the girl didn't recognise her out of uniform. She knew that she had been virtually invisible
while Louise was greeting her friend and smiling so
warmly at Mark when she visited Beverley Jakes at

Greenvale. She might not be so indifferent or so bored by an introduction to another woman if she knew that the man she had reserved for herself had been making light love to her on the previous evening, Gillian thought dryly.

As Robin suggested that they should combine forces for the remainder of the evening, she told herself that it was absurd to feel that Mark Barlow had deliberately manoeuvred matters to that end. For his cool gaze reduced her to the status of a stranger and there was only the merest courtesy in his deep drawl whenever he spoke to her. He was being very circumspect, she thought mockingly. He didn't want anything to upset the apple-cart just as he was about to get engaged to Hugh Penistone's daughter. He was possibly hoping that she wouldn't say or do anything that he'd have to explain away. Gillian was almost tempted to embarrass him!

Robin and Louise were members of the local tennis club and very keen players. They began to talk about a recent tournament and were soon so involved in friendly argument that their companions were forgotten.

Mark turned to Gillian and suggested that they should dance. She hesitated. He got to his feet with a slightly impatient air that indicated that he had no time for foolishness. Meekly she rose and accompanied him on to the dance floor and went into his waiting arms. She wished that her heart wouldn't tumble about in her breast so foolishly just because they closed about her as if she belonged in them until the end of time.

Dancing with him was sheer delight although he didn't dance as well as Robin and it took her a few moments to adjust her steps to his unfamiliar lead. She was very conscious of his masculinity, his attractiveness. She tried to hold herself slightly away, disturbed by the readiness of her body to react to his embrace.

He looked down at her with a faintly amused gleam in his grey eyes. 'You're looking very pretty this evening,' he said lazily.

It was impossible to know if he meant the words. She was instinctively suspicious of everything he said or did. Why should he wish to pay her even the slightest of compliments after all?

'Thank you,' she said stiffly.

'All for McAllister's benefit?'

She tensed at the hint of mockery. 'Of course. How could I have known that I was going to see you?' she retorted sweetly.

He smiled. 'Oh, I know you aren't interested in impressing me—except with your excellent work in the theatre. I might not have said much to you, Gillian, that isn't my way. But you'd have known soon enough if I wasn't well satisfied.'

She looked up at him. 'A little praise goes a long way, you know. Criticism, however justified, is always resented,' she said bluntly.

'My criticism is always justified.' The light tone mocked his own awareness of the arrogance that irritated her so much. 'Praise . . . ?' He smiled wryly. 'You'd have bridled if I'd dared to praise anything that's normal standards for a Kit's nurse. I've learned that much about you!'

Gillian smiled reluctantly. She knew he was right. She was as prickly as a hedgehog where Kit's was concerned, ready to take offence at the merest hint of a slight on the famous hospital's high standards of training.

The music was slow and very sensuous. He drew her

closer as they danced on the crowded floor and she was conscious of the warm sweetness of his breath on her cheek and hair, she quickened to the pressure of his lean body against her own. She knew that she shouldn't melt against him. It might seem like an invitation to continue where they had broken off on the previous evening.

As if he read her mind with disconcerting ease, he said quietly: 'I'm sorry about last night, Gillian. I guess I took too much for granted.'

She was astonished by the apology. She hadn't thought it possible that he was the kind of man to admit to being at fault. 'Yes, you did,' she agreed promptly, not too ready to forgive him.

'There's something about you that puzzles me,' he said slowly. 'I can't be sure if you're very innocent or very experienced.'

'You aren't likely to find out, are you?' she said tartly, angry that he should doubt that she wasn't the type to sleep around. She pulled herself out of his disturbing embrace. 'I'd like to sit down. I'm rather tired.' She stalked ahead of him to the table where Robin and Louise were still talking tennis.

They broke off as Gillian reached them. She sat down beside Robin. He turned to her with flattering promptness and slipped an arm about her shoulders. He smiled at her with such loving tenderness that she felt quite guilty about having enjoyed those few moments in another man's arms.

Mark Barlow stirred her to swift anger. But he also flooded her with a heady desire. She didn't believe it was loving in any shape or form. Love without liking was just not possible for her, she felt. It was simply a sexual awareness that he triggered whether or not she wanted it to happen. For the first time in her life, Gillian knew the power of passion and ached for the glorious fulfilment that she could find in his arms.

The sooner she conquered that wild, wanton desire for a man she didn't even like the safer she would be, she decided firmly. For it seemed that too many women had thrown themselves at Mark Barlow, with or without success, and he obviously despised them for it. She didn't mean to make the same mistake. She didn't want to be just a brief enchantment—for a sensual man. She wanted to be loved and needed for the rest of her life—and surely that was just what Robin was offering. She could be content and secure, married to Robin. Excitement was all very well but it didn't last, she told herself levelly.

Mark went to the bar for a fresh supply of drinks. Robin lifted an eyebrow at Gillian in almost imperceptible query and she gave a slight shake of her head, smiling. She didn't want to dance again just yet. He turned to Louise.

He was a very good dancer. Watching as he whirled his lovely partner about the floor in expert, slightly extravagant style, Gillian recalled that her friends had always envied her whenever Robin took her to a hospital dance. The eagerness with which Louise had accepted his invitation and the ease with which she followed his lead and his intricate footwork proved that they had danced together on many occasions.

He was obviously popular, well-liked. He had established himself in the town as a capable and caring GP and he had acquired some very influential friends in the process. One day in the not too distant future, he would probably be a pillar of local society. As an extremely eligible bachelor, he could probably take his pick from the pretty girls in the district. But it seemed that he still loved her, still wanted to marry her.

Gillian wondered why the prospect didn't delight her as it should. She wondered wryly if she was suited to marriage, to husband, home and family. She loved nursing. Greenvale seemed to promise a great deal of job satisfaction. She had been reluctant to give up her career to marry Robin, three years before. She was still reluctant. If she couldn't carry on nursing after marriage then she didn't feel that she was in any hurry to marry at all . . .

'I wonder what brought you to Greenvale,' Mark said softly, taking the chair by her side.

Gillian looked at him, startled. She had been so lost in her thoughts of an uncertain future that she hadn't noticed his approach with the tray of drinks.

'Sorry . . . ?'

'Was it McAllister?'

'Pure chance,' she retorted, proud. Did he think she was the kind of girl to run after any man?

'I'm not a great believer in chance,' he drawled.

She shrugged. 'I'm not very interested in your beliefs,' she said coldly.

'Then you don't want to hear that I do believe in unconscious association.' He sat back in his chair and swirled the whisky in his glass.

Gillian stiffened. 'Meaning?'

He regarded her thoughtfully. 'You've been ill, perhaps a litle depressed. Maybe there hasn't been anyone of importance in your life since you broke with McAllister. I think you were hoping to pick up old threads when you applied for a job in a town where a former flame happened to live.'

'You're mistaken. I didn't know that Robin lived anywhere near Greenvale.'

'I think you did,' he said quietly.

She was about to argue. Then her innate honesty came to the fore. 'Yes, I knew—three years ago when he left Kit's. I'd forgotten it completely.'

'Your conscious mind had forgotten it,' he amended.

Gillian glared at him. 'I'm not chasing him!' she said indignantly.

He smiled. 'There isn't any need, is there? He's standing still, waiting to be caught. Why didn't you marry him three years ago? Oh, don't tell me! I'm not really interested in your reasons,' he added indifferently. 'I expect they were valid at the time. You must be feeling very flattered that he still cares for you. Don't let it go to your head, will you?'

She was suddenly furious. 'Will you mind your own business!' she flared. 'What an impossible person you are! How dare you interfere in my personal life!'

'I don't want to lose a good theatre nurse just when I've found her,' he drawled lightly. 'You think *I'm* a chauvinist, don't you? Marry McAllister and see if he'll allow his wife to carry on with her own career.'

Before she could throw a retort at him, Robin and Louise came off the dance floor, hand in hand, laughing. She saw a faint frown in Mark's eyes and wondered if he was jealous of their obvious liking for each other.

It was difficult to imagine him as a man in love, she thought dryly. He was attentive to Louise but not in the least lover-like. She wondered if he really wanted to marry the beautiful girl or if it was just ambition. She felt that Louise was determined to marry him and wondered why. He was very attractive, very eligible. He wasn't *lovable*!

He didn't seem to notice that she was very annoyed with him. That was only one of the more infuriating traits in the man, she decided bitterly, forced to smile, to reply to remarks so obviously addressed to her that she couldn't ignore them. But she didn't have to dance with him.

Refusing his invitation meant that she couldn't instantly get up to dance with Robin. They were both disappointed. Damn Mark Barlow! He was out to ruin her evening, she thought crossly. She just didn't understand why he had attached himself and his girlfriend so firmly to them when any newly engaged couple ought to want to be on their own.

Listening to the conversation, she learned that it was Hugh Penistone's sixtieth birthday at the weekend. She supposed that the engagement announcement was being timed to coincide with it. Neither of them mentioned it. The whole town seemed to know but it was obviously still unofficial. Louise wasn't wearing a ring on the hand that she tucked into the surgeon's arm so possessively.

He smiled at her and then glanced across the table at Gillian, the smile lingering in his grey eyes. Her heart gave an odd little jump and for the first time she admitted the enchantment in that slow, warm smile and understood why so many women wanted him.

She looked away, troubled by the stirring of a new and unwelcome feeling. That smile hadn't even been meant for her, she reminded herself firmly. She was a fool to be so moved by its charm. She was worse than a fool if she allowed herself to love a man who meant to marry another woman . . .

It was late when Robin took her home. In the car, he put an arm about her and tentatively sought her lips. Gillian kissed him but her heart wasn't in it. She knew that he was waiting for her to ask him into the flat. She knew that he wanted to make love to her. He was very much in love and the years without her couldn't have been easy for him.

Gillian's heart went out to him with warm and tender affection. But her body shrank from the thought of his lovemaking. She knew that she couldn't respond as he would naturally wish—and she just wasn't ready to commit herself so irrevocably to any man.

Maybe she would marry Robin, given enough time to be sure that it was what she wanted and that they could be happy. But she didn't want to go to bed with him at this stage.

She kissed him again and laid her hand lightly along his cheek in a gesture of affection.

'I'm very tired, Robin,' she said gently. 'It's been a full day . . .'

He understood immediately. She knew he was disappointed but he didn't protest or argue or make any attempt at persuasion. Letting herself into the flat and turning for a last wave as his car drew away from the kerb, Gillian wondered if Mark Barlow would have been so easily deflected from his purpose if he had brought her home with the intention of making love to her.

She felt rather guilty at the realisation that she might not have sent *him* away with so little regret.

She didn't dare to wonder if she would have sent him away at all . . .

CHAPTER NINE

THE next morning Gillian reported for work on the female surgical floor, carefully punctual. When Helen Irving left Greenvale at the end of the month, she would take over her job as senior theatre nurse, working in close liaison with Mark and Steve as a professional team. In the meantime, it was arranged that she should stand in for Helen on her off-duty days.

Things were working out quite well, Gillian decided. It suited her to have a brief breathing space to adjust to the new job and new colleagues and to be sure that she was really fit for the demands of working in Theatre. And it would give her more time to adjust to the way she felt about Mark.

That feeling was disturbing and dangerous, and much too persistent for her liking. She found that she was thinking about him instead of her work, very often. She found that she was remembering too vividly everything he had said and done in the short time that she had known him, little of it endearing yet apparently unforgettable. She found that her body could still quicken at the memory of his touch, his kiss, his nearness. She might despise that weakness in herself, but that didn't stop the wanting, she thought ruefully.

It was infuriating to recall her scornful contempt for the many women who sighed over the handsome surgeon and realise that she was just as foolish. Heaven knew what it was about the man but he certainly exercised a very potent magic and Gillian determined to keep him safely at arms' length. For there could be no future in wanting a man like Mark Barlow.

She didn't love him. She might have been able to understand and forgive that wanton weakness for him if she had fallen in love with Mark. But as he just wasn't the kind of man that she could ever truly like or admire let alone love, it was despicable that he could fill her with that tempestuous, throbbing desire. She didn't mean to give way to it. She hoped that he wouldn't offer her any more temptation . . .

It was a novel experience for Gillian to be nursing patients after she had assisted at their operations. At Kit's, she had seldom seen them before their brief sojourn in Theatre. After surgery, they had been returned to the dedicated care of the ward staff. She found that she liked the continuity and the greater involvement with the patients.

Beverley Jakes was not a good patient, however. She was making a great deal of fuss about a very minor gynaecological correction. She insisted that she was in pain while showing very little evidence of it and she obviously intended to enjoy a lengthy and quite unnecessary stay. She rang her bell constantly and for the most trivial of reasons.

Gillian had nursed private patients before and knew that they could be difficult and demanding. She didn't mind the extra work. She did mind that Beverley behaved as though she was a domestic servant entirely at her back and call throughout the day. Being a well-trained nurse, she smiled and said nothing as she retrieved a magazine from the floor or passed a box of tissues that was within reach, or adjusted the window blind or plumped pillows or poured fresh orange juice for a patient perfectly able to do such things for herself. But she seethed, deep down.

The spoiled, self-centred Beverley was not only ungrateful for everything that was done for her, constantly finding fault, she was also a snob. She looked down her slender nose at Gillian and the other nurses in their pale green uniforms, talking down to them with a very irritating condescension in voice and manner. She was much disliked.

Gillian had never allowed such people to get under her skin in the past. During five years of nursing in a big hospital, she had met all kinds and learned to accept and understand different types of behaviour. Now, she wondered if she disliked and resented Beverley so much because Mark seemed to like her and find her amusing. He seemed to be in and out of her room quite unnecessarily during those first few days after the girl's operation.

Surgeons at Kit's had their housemen on the wards who saw much more of the patients than they did, making routine rounds to check and report on progress. At Greenvale, it was apparently Mark's practice at least to be in constant and reassuring touch with his patients. People who were paying for the privilege of his surgical attention liked to feel that they were getting value for money, of course.

And Beverley was a personal friend who basked in the flattering warmth of his liking and concern and frequent attention.

By contrast, Mrs Maddox was a pleasure to nurse. She was so cheerful and uncomplaining, so friendly and so interested in everyone, a real favourite with the nurses who wouldn't have minded how many demands she made on them. In fact, she was shy of asking for even the smallest of services. Everyone was anxious to do as much as possible for her as a result. Gillian liked her very much and made excuses to enter her room during the day for a few moments of relaxed chat.

In all fairness, she had to admit that Mark was as attentive to one patient as the other, even if he did seem to lack the traditional type of bedside manner. She felt he was brusque with Mrs Maddox. The big woman was making satisfactory progress after the hysterectomy and Mark was reassuring about the condition of her heart. But high blood pressure was causing some anxiety and there were other problems due to her obesity. He was impatient with her apparent inability to observe the diet he had prescribed for her and which she circumvented via her husband and various visiting friends.

Mrs Maddox only chuckled when he scolded, made any number of promises for the future, and reached for a forbidden fancy as soon as he was out of sight. She had been fat all her life, she declared happily, and didn't know why everyone made such a fuss about it.

After the surgeon's visits, she seemed quite unable to talk sensibly about anything but his good looks, his charm, his cleverness and, more often, his rumoured wedding plans, for some considerable time. Those were the times when Gillian found that she was much too busy to stay and listen.

On one such occasion, he came back into the room as Gillian finished making the big woman comfortable against her pillows, meaning to make her escape before she could get into full stride.

If Mark knew that his patient was enthusing about him as he walked in, it didn't show in his expression. He had returned for his pen, left lying on the bedside table. It was slim, gold and very distinctive. A present from a grateful patient, one of the nurses had said, referring to the expensive pen. A present from a grateful Louise, another nurse had amended with a cynical laugh. Whichever it was, he seemed to value it.

'You wouldn't like to lose that, I daresay,' Mrs Maddox said with a knowing smile as he restored it carefully to his breast pocket, betraying that she also assumed that it had been a gift from the girl he planned to marry.

'It has a certain sentimental value, I must admit,' he agreed carelessly.

'Men are more sentimental than women about such things. Don't you think so, Nurse?' Mrs Maddox appealed to Gillian, busily tidying the array of books and magazines that lay on a table by the window.

Glancing round, she met Mark's indifferent gaze. He wasn't interested in her opinion. He wasn't interested in her any more. He had virtually ignored her since that evening at the Country Club. Gillian wondered if she had slapped him down a little too hard. It was much more likely that she had been a very fleeting fancy for a sensual man, forgotten in the excitement of his soon to be announced engagement.

'It depends on the man,' she returned lightly. 'Most of them aren't at all sentimental, in my experience.' Something in her tone implied her doubt that Mark ever indulged in any kind of sentiment. He was a hard man who didn't make allowances, didn't believe in compromise and didn't forgive easily, she thought with a hard little lump of resentment in her breast.

Mark moved from the bed with a slight air of impatience. As he did so, his eye was caught by a colourful box of sweets, still in its cellophane wrapper, that had slipped into view as Mrs Maddox shifted incautiously on her pillows.

He paused.

He looked down at the sweets with a slightly raised eyebrow, visibly annoyed. 'I don't remember that they were included on your diet sheet, Mrs Maddox,' he said coldly.

She flushed like a naughty child caught in mischief. The tone of his voice was an unmistakable rebuke. Her hand moved instinctively to push the box out of sight, faltered, flew to clutch at her throat in dismay.

'Oh, I didn't mean to eat them,' she said hastily, palpably resorting to an untruth. 'My husband brought them in for Nurse Grant. I was just about to give them to her when you came back.' She caught up the sweets in both hands and thrust them at Gillian who had hurried to the side of the bed at first sign of her distress. 'Here you are, dear! You don't have to worry about dieting with that lovely figure. Just enjoy them!'

Gillian took the sweets with a slightly defiant glance at the surgeon. 'Thank you very much, Mrs Maddox . . .'

A nerve was throbbing in his lean cheek. He was very angry. 'I'm obliged to give you the benefit of the doubt, Mrs Maddox,' he said curtly. 'But I shall see to it that your husband doesn't bring in any more sweets—for you or the nurses. We are trying to keep temptation out of your way, after all.' He strode to the door. 'May I have a word, Nurse Grant!' It was not a request. 'Now, if you don't mind,' he added sharply as she seemed to hesitate.

Gillian bridled. But they couldn't indulge in a slanging

match before the patient. She smiled reassuringly at the anxious Mrs Maddox. 'I'll be back in a moment . . .'

'Oh, my dear! Have I done the wrong thing?' the big woman whispered urgently, catching at Gillian's hand. 'Mustn't I give you presents? Is it against the rules?'

'Nurse Grant!'

Gillian swung round at that peremptory use of her name. He was holding the door open, eyes hard with anger. She flashed him a militant look and walked towards him, fuming at his tone.

Out in the corridor with the door firmly closed and no one else apparently within earshot, she turned on him. 'You'll lose all your patients if you insist on frightening them to death!' she said indignantly. 'You were an absolute pig to that poor woman!'

'That poor woman is eating herself into an early grave. With your assistance, apparently,' he said angrily. 'Sweets! You might as well allow her to swallow poison! What kind of a nurse are you to turn a blind eye to such blatant contempt for my advice?'

Gillian flushed 'I didn't know that she had them,' she retorted defensively.

'It's your business to know! The woman's a fool who can't be convinced that fat can be fatal—and probably will be in her case! Fools need to be protected from themselves and that's part of your job while she's here and in your care!'

'You don't have to tell me about my duties as a nurse!' she flared, sensitive as always to the least criticism of her Kit's training.

'It seems that I do,' he returned coldly. 'You can't stop her from having visitors. You can see to it that they don't smuggle poison in with them. I shall hold you respon-

sible if Mrs Maddox puts on one more ounce. You won't
be surprised to learn that I can influence your dismissal
from Greenvale and the improbability of your employ-
ment by any other nursing establishment in the country!'

It was savage. Gillian stared, buffeted by the force of
the threat, feeling as if a brutal hand had suddenly
grasped her by the heart as she met the cold, implacable
contempt in the grey eyes.

'Nothing about you could surprise me,' she retorted,
with spirit if a little unsteadily. 'I only have to remind
myself that you're all the things I most dislike bound up
in one person!' She walked away from him, trembling.

Mark looked after her, a tautness in his tall frame, a
tension about his handsome mouth. He had wanted to
hurt her and he knew that he had done so. But there
wasn't the slightest satisfaction in his revenge for rebuffs
that he should have been able to shrug off with his usual
indifference.

I hate him, Gillian fumed. *I hate him! How dare he
speak to me so!* But, deep down, waves of hurt were
rippling through her that someone she had been foolishly beginning to like, to allow into her heart, should prove
just as horrid and hateful as she had first thought. She
was disappointed. She had been given an occasional
glimpse of the man he could be and then discovered that
it was all foolish fancy on her part. Because he was
attractive, because he stirred her senses in a way that no
other man did, she had been too ready to forget those
first and obviously reliable impressions. On her very first
day at Greenvale, she had known he was an arrogant,
uncaring brute who would trample on anyone's feelings.

Gillian was quick and proud and passionate. She
didn't care that a Kit's nurse never exchanged angry

words with a highly-qualified and much-respected surgeon within sight and sound of his patients and other members of the staff. She didn't care if he could have her sacked. She didn't want to stay at Greenvale if he meant to persist in treating her like dirt, she told herself, fighting the tears that ought not to be thrusting themselves into her eyes. She didn't mean to let a man like Mark Barlow reduce her to tears, she declared proudly.

She left the offending box of sweets in the nurses' room for the benefit of her colleagues. She didn't want them. She didn't feel that Mrs Maddox was to blame for that sudden spat between herself and the surgeon. He seemed to seize on the smallest excuse to humiliate her, she thought bitterly. He just didn't like her at all—any more than she liked him!

On her way back to Mrs Maddox, knowing that the big woman was probably worrying about the result of the gift she had been forced to make, she met Penny. The older girl glanced at her curiously.

'You seem to have made an enemy out of our Mark,' she said, smiling.

Gillian shrugged. 'I didn't want him as a friend, anyway,' she returned with careful casualness.

'The whole place is buzzing. You aren't wise to row with him where everyone can hear, you know. The powers-that-be don't like friction between the staff.'

'He chose the venue!'

'*Did* you two know each other? Before you came to Greenvale, I mean? You don't behave like strangers,' Penny said lightly.

'I never met him until I came here, I told you.' Gillian didn't want to discuss her reaction to the surgeon. She liked Penny, got on well with her, but had quickly learned that she was indiscreet. Her tongue ran away with her and she repeated confidences before she realised it. Gillian had never been a girl to talk about herself very much. She knew that Penny thought she was rather too reserved.

During the rest of the day, she was aware of a hum of speculation and curious glances. Rising above it, she got on with her work and tried not to think about Mark Barlow. Thinking about him and the way he had spoken, the way he had looked, only depressed her spirits.

He was tinkering with the engine of his Mercedes when Gillian made her way across the car park towards her Mini at the end of the day. She was in a hurry to get home because she was going out with Robin.

Having seen him from a distance, she was careful not to glance at the surgeon as she drew near, her heart welling up with the resentment and pain that she had been keeping firmly at bay since their clash.

As she passed his car, he stepped back from the engine, wiping his hands on an old rag, and saw the slight girl in her green frock and sensible shoes. 'Gillian!' he exclaimed quickly.

She didn't turn. It infuriated her that he had always used her first name as though he had every right to do so. It infuriated her even more that his use of it now implied that he had dismissed their earlier encounter as though it had never happened.

She found that her fingers were trembling so much as she tried to insert the key in the lock that it fell to the ground. She stooped to pick it up, annoyed with herself for her foolish reaction to his unexpected presence in the car park. He had usually left the clinic by this time.

She knew he was walking towards her with the intention of speaking. She wanted to escape before he realised that she was flustered, much too aware of him, dreading another argument. She hated their angry encounters. It seemed that there had been so many of them. Why couldn't they be friends? Why couldn't he like her?

He reached her side as she opened the car door. 'Gillian . . .'

She glanced at him with dislike. 'I'm in a hurry,' she said coldly.

'Apologising only takes a moment,' he told her quietly.

Gillian's hackles rose. 'If you're expecting an apology from me then you're about to be disappointed,' she flared.

He smiled, rather wry. 'Wrong way round.' He hesitated, wondering why he went on wanting this girl with so little encouragement. 'I was too hard on you. I'm afraid I lost my temper. I'm sorry.'

Gillian stared. He was the last man in the world she would have expected to admit to being at fault. 'Oh . . .' she said lamely, not knowing what else to say.

'I'm not sure what was actually said at the time,' he admitted, rather rueful. 'Far too much, I daresay. I hope you'll forget it.'

She was troubled by the muddle of her emotions as he stood looking down at her, almost but not quite smiling, almost but not quite friendly. It didn't occur to her that he was finding it very difficult to swallow his pride for the sake of a very unfamiliar feeling for a girl he scarcely knew. She merely thought that he found it very difficult to speak to her with any degree of warmth or liking.

He was an enigma, she thought heavily, torn between

a lingering anger and that tug at her heart that was so inexplicable. She didn't understand him at all. She didn't understand what he did to her emotions, turning them topsy-turvy. It was too frightening, too much of a threat to her peace of mind and her hope of happiness with Robin or any other man. Perhaps it was just as well that they weren't friends or ever likely to be . . .

She got into the car as though it was a refuge, a sanctuary. Certainly she felt safer with that little distance between them. She gripped the steering wheel with both hands so that she shouldn't be tempted to reach out and reassure him with a forgiving and perhaps betraying touch.

'I'm quick-tempered myself,' she said carefully. It was the nearest she could come to accepting his apology.

He rested a hand on the car roof and leaned down to her. 'Come and have some tea with me,' he invited. 'Then I'll know I'm forgiven. I'll take you to an old-fashioned tea-shop that serves the best cream cakes in the country.'

Gillian's heart thumped. He was the most unpredictable man she had ever known, she thought, shaken by the unexpected warmth of persuasion in his deep voice. How could any girl ever know where she was with him?

'Sorry. I haven't the time,' she said, starting up the car. 'Another day, perhaps . . .' She kept her tone very light. She didn't want him to know that she was terribly tempted. She was level-headed enough to realise the dangers in yielding to even the smallest temptation where he was concerned.

He was too attractive. Even when she was hating and despising him and wishing she had never met him . . .

Another rebuff—and richly deserved this time, Mark

thought wryly, looking after the little Mini with the stubborn, spirited girl at the wheel. She was prickly with a pride that he understood because it burned so fiercely in his own breast. But that understanding didn't seem to be of much help when it came to overcoming it.

For the first time in his life, Mark was utterly at a loss when it came to a woman he had not expected to matter to him so much so soon . . .

Gillian let herself into the flat that had quickly become home and unpacked the shopping that she had collected on the way from the clinic, trying not to regret her refusal of a cream tea. It had been an unusual kind of olive branch, she thought dryly. But Mark Barlow was an unusual man.

Thrusting him to the back of her mind, she busied herself about the flat until it should be time to dress for her evening with Robin.

Gillian hadn't seen as much of him as she would have liked, affection revived and memories stirred by their reunion. He was not only a busy doctor in general practice, he was also on several local committees. He was a keen member of the tennis club. He was interested in amateur dramatics and was currently involved in rehearsals for a production at the Civic Theatre. Since coming to live with his uncle in the bustling market town, he had made many new friends and found many new interests.

Gillian wondered if she could fit into his new life if she did marry him—and if there would be any room for her! She didn't doubt that he still loved her. Robin was the kind to love only once and for ever, she felt. She also felt that he managed to be reasonably content without a wife in his life. She might be a very useful asset. She didn't believe she was essential to his happiness. So perhaps she needn't feel too guilty if she decided that she didn't want to spend the rest of her life with him.

Mark had been right in one respect, she recalled, a little wryly. Sounding Robin on the subject of working wives, as casually as she could, she had learned that he would expect his wife to stay at home and busy herself with looking after him and the house and the eventual children. Quite obviously, he felt that marriage ought to contain quite enough interest and excitement for any woman.

Gillian instinctively rebelled. She just couldn't imagine herself relegated to the rôle of housewife and mother, however worthy, when she was a trained nurse who not only loved her job but knew she was good at it.

If she married Robin, he would simply have to accept that she meant to continue with her nursing career until she had children and return to it as soon as they reached school age. She didn't intend to waste the years of hard work and dedication that had resulted in the proud possession of her Kit's badge, she thought, a little defiantly.

Thinking of it, she instinctively lifted a hand to finger the small, silver and very distinctive badge that she always wore pinned to the breast of her uniform frock.

It was missing.

Gillian was utterly dismayed and very distressed. She turned the flat upside down, looking for it. She searched the interior of the Mini, in vain. She racked her brain to remember when and where it might have fallen from her frock and her heart grew heavier as she realised that it had possibly gone for ever.

Robin was sympathetic when he arrived to find that the hunt for her badge had delayed her in getting ready for the evening with him. But he didn't seem to realise just how much it meant to her. It stood for five years of her life, after all . . .

CHAPTER TEN

GILLIAN had never been a girl to cry over spilled milk. So she made light of her loss and wouldn't allow it to spoil the evening for herself and Robin.

Abandoning the obviously futile search for the precious badge, she hurried away to change into a black velvet evening skirt, appliqued with bright flowers, and a filmy black chiffon blouse with scooped neckline and puffed sleeves. Black accentuated the fairness of hair and skin, the delicate purity of her features, the vivid blue of her eyes. She wore her hair loose, curling lightly on her shoulders, knowing that was the way Robin liked it.

Seeing the look in his eyes when she came back to join him, ready for the evening, she knew that she was pretty for him and she was glad. Impulsively, she leaned over to kiss him, heart very full with the lingering affection that she felt for him that could never be loving, after all. Robin had played an important part in her youthful hopes and dreams of happiness. It was no one's fault that the man in her dreams had unexpectedly taken on someone else's face and hair and tall frame.

They had been invited to a party and Gillian was introduced to several of Robin's friends. He was attentive, very affectionate, openly proud of his pretty companion. She had already discovered that he was a popular personality and his gentle hints at a wedding in the not too distant future seemed to meet with general approval. Gillian tried not to feel that he was committing her to an engagement before she was ready.

It was an enjoyable evening until she saw Mark, talking to a very pretty girl in pink. He was haunting her, she thought ruefully. She couldn't seem to escape him. In such a small community with its limited social circles, she supposed it was inevitable that they should meet often at parties, at clubs, at organised functions in the district. It was going to be hard on her emotions but excellent for her self-control, she told herself wryly.

She had just left a group of people to go in search of Robin who had wandered off for fresh drinks some time previously and obviously been side-tracked. She hesitated at the sight of Mark, instantly recognising the tall, dark-haired and much too attractive man in the casual blue jeans and sweater.

As though he had sensed her gaze and her hesitation, he glanced towards her. Gillian's heart jumped as she saw the quickening of interest in his grey eyes. Almost immediately, he said something to the girl by his side and then left her to thread his way through the crowded mass of people. It was too late for Gillian to pretend that she hadn't seen him.

'I didn't expect to see you here,' he said without preliminary.

It was impossible to know if he was pleased or not. If she hadn't glimpsed that brief warmth in his eyes, she might have been chilled and dismayed by the impersonal tone and manner.

'It's a small world,' she said tritely. She smiled at him rather more warmly than she had intended. Then, anxious to assure him that she didn't need or want him to dance attendance on her because of a chance meeting, feeling that her smile might have been too warm, too encouraging, she said hastily: 'I'm with Robin.'

He nodded indifferently. 'Warn me if I'm likely to tread on him,' he said in his lazy drawl.

Gillian stared. 'Sorry . . . ?'

'I take it he's invisible this evening. Most doctors would envy him the gift,' he declared, very dry.

She laughed. 'He *is* here. Getting drinks. Don't be absurd!'

He was delighted with that little gurgle of laughter. He wondered if the way to this girl's heart was through her sense of humour, so quickly sparked by his own. He reached for the wallet that he carried in the back pocket of his trousers, took something out of it. 'I believe this belongs to you.'

Gillian held out her hand instinctively. He dropped the small silver badge into her palm and her fingers tightened over it thankfully.

'Oh, I am grateful to you!' she said warmly. 'Where did you find it? I've been hunting high and low all evening. I was so sure that I'd never see it again!'

He smiled at her fervour. 'It was in the car park. I happened to spot it just after you drove away. At first, I thought it was a coin of sorts and almost didn't bother to pick it up.'

'I'm so glad you did! You don't know what it means to me, Mark!' she exclaimed.

He looked down at her, thoughtful. 'You don't know what it means to *me* to hear my name on your lips at last,' he drawled, gently teasing her insistence on formality, her persistent refusal to admit him to her friendship with that small concession.

Gillian blushed. 'Oh, I don't believe that!' she declared defensively, taken by surprise.

'You should.' He turned to look around the room. 'McAllister's getting you a drink, is he? With any luck, he'll be called out to an emergency. Then the evening won't be entirely wasted for either of us,' he said lightly.

Gillian looked at him, quickly indignant. About to blast him with a scathing put-down, the words died on her lips as she met the warmth in his eyes. 'I don't know where I am with you,' she said instead, helplessly, melting before the man's magnetism.

'*I* don't know where you are, either,' he retorted, very dry. 'Sometimes you're a thorn in my side. Sometimes you're simply on my mind. But you certainly seem to be under my skin in one way or another since you came here. I could have done without you in my life at this particular time, Gillian.'

She knew that the blunt words referred to the engagement to Louise Penistone that was hanging over his head like the Sword of Damocles.

'I'm not in your life,' she said coolly, trying to keep resentment out of her tone. 'We aren't even friends . . .'

He put his hand to the nape of her neck and his touch sent a tingling down her spine. He looked down at her with a glow in his eyes that made her pulses quicken. 'What the hell has friendship to do with the way we feel about each other?' he asked, very soft.

Gillian was shocked into silence. He was too direct—and he ought not to know that her body leaped at his touch. But he did know and she couldn't deny it for all her pride. She stood very still, fighting the dangerous desire that he evoked, yielding at last to the truth about her feeling for this man that she had been resisting for days.

'Gillian . . . ?'

Her name was a velvet caress. She met his eyes and was lost. Her body melted and her heart tumbled in her breast. She knew that she loved him. *He* was her destiny, her love. Suddenly it didn't seem to matter that he didn't love her and that he would soon be celebrating his engagement to the lovely Louise.

He bent his dark head. His lips brushed the wing of pale hair, the delicate shell of her ear. 'We've wasted too much time already,' he murmured, warm and persuasive. 'Ditch McAllister and let's get out of here.'

Gillian wanted to go with him. She wanted to be in his arms, to know his kisses and caresses, to drown in the deep waters of their mutual desire. She wanted the ecstasy that he promised with the look in his eyes and the urgency in his deep voice. She was all kinds of a fool but she loved him and she longed for the little he was offering. It might be all she would ever know of happiness with this infuriating, irresistible man . . .

She saw Robin, drinks in hand, pausing to speak to a friend as he made his way back to her. He looked so happy that her heart smote her. He was totally unaware of the emotional tensions that had vibrated between herself and Mark for days. She was suddenly flooded with guilt because she didn't love Robin and would never marry him. She couldn't humiliate him before his friends into the bargain! She had come to this party with a man who made no secret of his hope of marrying her. It was quite impossible for her to leave with a man who cherished hopes of a very different kind.

'I can't,' she said slowly. 'You know that I can't . . .'

Mark didn't hear the regret behind the words. He only heard the slight defiance in her tone and felt that he had been rebuffed yet again. Too proud to show hurt or dismay, he shrugged and dropped his hand from her neck.

Gillian felt that he took away much more than the touch of his hand and her heart sank. The barrier had come down between them with a kind of finality that made her despair. He might not give her another chance to show that she cared—and she couldn't run after him. Every girl had her pride and Gillian had rather more than most.

He moved away with a nod for Robin who was associate rather than friend. Robin assumed that he had merely been exchanging pleasantries with Gillian. He didn't regard the surgeon as a threat. She so obviously didn't like the man. He was much more anxious about her relationship with Steve Palmer who was something of a Casanova and seemed to be spending too much time in her company. She encouraged him because she liked him.

Robin wasn't as confident as he seemed about the future. Gillian wasn't exactly keeping him at a distance, but he was conscious of a slight reserve that warned him not to rush his fences. It took time to bridge the gap of a three-year separation. Their lives had followed separate paths in that time. Gillian had become even more independent and even more dedicated to her work. But after three years of hopeless loving, he felt he could wait a little longer for the happiness that they would eventually have together. He was prepared to give her the year at Greenvale if that was what she wanted. Then she might be ready to settle down to being a doctor's wife.

Talking to Robin, Gillian was conscious that Mark had returned to the side of the pretty girl in pink. She tried not to watch the obvious progress that led to his eventual departure from the party with her. His going didn't ruin her evening. It had been ruined when he walked away from her so dismissively . . .

He continued to be a regular visitor to the floor where she was working. When it was remarked upon by another nurse, Gillian realised that it wasn't his usual practice. It seemed that Beverley Jakes must be the magnet that drew him. Passing the girl's room as she went about the day's work, she often heard his deep drawl and Beverley's light voice in reply, followed by a ripple of shared laughter.

He spent a lot of time talking to the girl, teasing her, encouraging her and indulging her in rather indiscreet flirtation. He didn't behave at all like a man on the verge of committing himself to marriage with another woman, Gillian thought dryly and with a foolish little flicker of hope in her heart.

Beverley always looked like a cat that had been at the cream after his visits—and he came out of her room with a smile in his grey eyes that didn't always fade instantly at sight of Gillian if they chanced to meet in the corridor. That smile, evoked by another girl's attraction for him, was cold comfort but she found herself looking for it with a lift of her heavy heart.

Somehow they ran into each other quite often. Gillian wouldn't accept that she contrived some of those brief encounters. It *was* chance that she had chosen just that moment to make her way to a patient's room with a prepared injection or a milk feed or a change of linen, she told herself firmly. She *wasn't* hovering in the hope of seeing and speaking to him!

They were unsatisfactory encounters, anyway. Sometimes he smiled and greeted her coolly before walking on. Sometimes he paused for a few words, casual and quite unimportant and often only concerned with the progress of his patients. But usually Gillian just glanced at him and hurried on her way, unsmiling, incensed by his readiness to encourage a patient in most unethical flirtation, anxious that he shouldn't suspect how her heart lurched with longing for just one more chance of happiness, however fleeting. He didn't mean to offer it, it seemed. Perhaps the pretty girl in pink had compensated him for any disappointment he might have felt. Perhaps Beverley Jakes was more amusing, more attractive, after all. Perhaps he had simply decided against getting involved in any way with a nurse—and particularly a Greenvale nurse.

However it was, time was running out. Hugh Penistone's birthday with its special celebration party was fast approaching and it seemed that everyone knew that his daughter's engagement was to be announced on that occasion. Greenvale, like Kit's, revelled in gossip about members of its staff and Mark Barlow's ambitions were obviously no secret.

Gillian tried to stifle the pain and dismay she felt that his plans for the future certainly didn't include her and she turned gratefully to the comfort that Robin and Steve offered during those first difficult days of knowing that she had fallen in love with a man who would never love her.

She knew that Steve liked and admired her very much. She didn't think that he meant to fall in love with her and she was thankful. Robin loved her too much and that made her feel guilty, knowing that she would never care enough to marry him. Perhaps she should never have met Mark Barlow and discovered just what had always been missing from her feelings for Robin and every other man. Love without sexual longing was a romantic theory that didn't promise to be very lasting, Gillian decided, facing up to facts. Sexual desire without love had proved to be impossible for her, after all.

She didn't know why she loved Mark. He was arrogant, autocratic. He wasn't endearing. He was cold and critical and contemptuous. He took too much for granted. But there had been moments when she felt that he could be a very different man; caring and concerned, warm and tender and reassuring, kind and thoughtful, if he ever allowed himself to love.

It was that other Mark, so well hidden from the world by a cloak of arrogance and reserve, that Gillian had recognised and instinctively loved long before she admitted that her dislike of him was just a defence for her too-vulnerable heart. She hadn't wanted to accept that he was the man she was destined to love. For she had known from the first that she had little chance of happiness with such a man.

Loving him, longing for him, pretending not to care that he flirted with other girls and meant to marry Louise, she went about her work at Greenvale with a smile carefully pinned to her lips and an apparently light heart. She was thankful for the training that had taught her to discipline her emotions and push personal problems to the back of her mind when she was on duty. She was thankful for the pride that protected her from hurling herself at his head like too many other women.

Later that week, she was sent to Theatre for the day to stand in for Helen Irving who was off duty.

Preparing the theatre and the necessary equipment for the day's list, longer than usual, she was almost too busy to notice Mark's arrival. She was checking the array of instruments and swabs and gallipots on a prepared trolley, mentally running over the procedure for the first operation on the list, when he paused by her side on his way to the changing-room.

'Good morning, Gillian. Everything under control?'

'Certainly,' she returned lightly, chin tilting as though something in his tone had doubted her efficiency. In fact, he was almost friendly. It was the first sign of a thaw in days.

'Good. I've changed the running order, by the way. Sorry it's short notice. I've decided to do the breast biopsy first thing. I've a feeling it will lead to a partial mastectomy at least. It might even need a radical.'

She looked at him quickly. 'You'll carry on if it proves necessary?'

'We've Mrs Hume's permission to do so and it will spare the traumatic build-up to another operation. Steve can keep her lightly under while we wait for the lab result and they've promised to rush it through. She's very anxious to get it over, of course. Women care deeply about these things, don't they?' In his deep voice was the warm understanding and the genuine compassion that every good surgeon must possess.

Gillian nodded. 'Most women are very brave, I've always found. But it seems to leave psychological scars that last much longer than the surgical ones . . . losing a breast.' She gave an unprofessional little shudder. 'I'd hate it myself. And Mrs Hume isn't very much older than I am, is she?'

'Twenty-eight. It's very unfortunate. But she seems to

be facing up to the threat very sensibly. She'll need
sympathetic nursing and a lot of help from her husband if
I'm right.'

He watched while Gillian counted swabs. He was very
conscious of the femininity of her slight figure in the
loose green gown of a theatre nurse, most of her pale
hair hidden by the loose cap. He was enchanted by the
fair prettiness of her small face, the delicate features and
striking blue eyes that could be too expressive, leaving
him in no doubt that her feelings were very mixed where
he was concerned.

She was on his mind, day and night. Wanting her was a
torment. Constantly threaded through that fierce desire
was a strong strand of need that deepened with every
passing day. He had always been utterly self-sufficient,
needing no one, content with his bachelor way of life and
cherishing his freedom. Since meeting Gillian, he had
discovered that there was something lacking in his life,
after all. He wasn't yet ready to commit himself entirely
and irrevocably to loving her. But he was very near to it.

It was damnable that she continued to deny the existence of a flame of mutual attraction that had leaped to
life almost at their first meeting and burned fiercely ever
since. It was frustrating that she rebuffed every attempt
on his part to bring them closer with the inevitable and
very necessary result.

Mark was a proud man. He had never found it necessary to swallow his pride to get what he wanted from life,
women or anything else. But Gillian was a very special
woman. She seemed to be more important to him than
his pride. So he would have to go on trying to win her
liking and respect and friendship even at the risk of
further rebuffs.

He had never been a patient man. But what Gillian offered promised to be worth all the waiting that it took.

'How do you feel? Any nerves?' he asked lightly.

'None at all. You've forgotten that I'm very used to theatre work,' she said briskly, knowing she mustn't warm to the unexpected smile in his eyes or the friendliness in his voice. He would only disappoint her again.

'And getting used to me?' he suggested. 'You've already had the worst of my tongue and my temper, after all.' He smiled. 'You know me better than you did if not as well as I'd hoped.'

Gillian glanced at him, a little colour stealing into her face. He sounded regretful. But he had quickly consoled himself with the pretty girl in pink—and he had certainly been flirting with Beverley Jakes for days. How could she believe that he was genuinely interested in her—or that he promised anything but a few golden hours in his arms?

'I may know you better. I don't trust you any more than I ever did,' she said slowly.

'Could it be that you don't trust your own feelings, Gillian?' He was direct.

She was silent, checking the carefully labelled hypodermic syringes with their dosages of different drugs that were always kept in readiness for any emergency while the patient was on the operating table.

Steve came through the swing doors from one of the ante-rooms, gowned and booted, ready for the day's work, his auburn hair rebelling beneath the green cap and gleaming in the bright overhead lighting.

'Chatting up my girl again!' he demanded in mock outrage, eyes dancing. 'Hands off! Anyway, you're too late. She's going out with me tonight.'

Mark smiled thinly and strode away to scrub-up, abruptly reminded that a patient would soon be needing his attention, his surgical skill and his entire concentration. An operating theatre was not the place to talk his way into Gillian's favour—and it seemed that he couldn't compete with the light and obviously successful touch of his colleague.

However light-hearted he might be about everything else, Steve took his job very seriously. He went over to the complicated arrangement of valves and cylinders that were his responsibility and began to check that everything was in order before the arrival of the first patient on that morning's list.

Gillian hurried away to explain to the rest of the theatre staff that Mrs Hume was first on the list instead of the appendicectomy they had been expecting. She rang down to check that the patient had been given the pre-med in good time and asked the nurse in charge to send her up to Theatre without delay.

Mrs Hume was received in an ante-room by the surgeon and his anaesthetist. She was drowsy from the pre-med, quite untroubled by anxiety, sure that she would be in good hands. Within seconds, she was deeply asleep from the injection that Steve had skilfully given into her hand while he talked to her reassuringly.

She was taken into the theatre and lifted on to the table and Gillian prepared the site of the biopsy for the surgeon's knife. Steve was busy with the anaesthetising process.

Mask in position, Mark waited for the go-ahead from his colleague. Gillian stepped back from the operating table. He glanced at her and she nodded to indicate that the preparations were complete and everything was in readiness for the operation.

For a moment, tense and expectant, their eyes met and held above the green masks. Grey eyes looked deep into blue, seeking a glimmer of a smile, a trace of encouragement that would allow him to hope that he was more important than the other men in her life.

Gillian's heart trembled suddenly. There was a glow, a fire, a flame in his eyes that she had never seen before.

It was gone in a moment.

For Steve spoke, lightly declaring that the patient was well and truly under and there were no problems.

Mark turned to his work, suddenly impersonal.

Gillian became so absorbed that she quite forgot to be emotionally involved with the man behind the mask. For the time being, he was just a skilled surgeon and she was a trained nurse who efficiently anticipated and supplied his every need.

It was neither the time nor the place to wish that he needed her beyond the coldly clinical surroundings of an operating theatre . . .

CHAPTER ELEVEN

GILLIAN enjoyed the evening with Steve. He took her to a concert at the Floral Hall in the nearby seaside town. They had a similar taste in music. They seemed to have lots of things in common and he had become a very good friend.

After the busy day in Theatre, she was glad to relax in his undemanding company. He was so nice, so easy to be with. She liked him and she appreciated his lightness of heart and his easy handling of their relationship.

By unspoken consent, they didn't talk about Greenvale or Mark Barlow or the day's work. There were times when Gillian wondered if Steve was sensitive to her unwilling love for the surgeon. She was just a little surprised that this man with a reputation for being something of a Casanova made so few demands on her. His kisses were light and merely affectionate, entirely acceptable to her. She never felt that he regarded her as a possible sexual conquest. He was either content to keep things on a friendly footing—or he was biding his time.

She wished that she could keep all her relationships with men on such a comfortable basis for the time being. She just wasn't ready for loving with all its difficulties and demands, she mourned ruefully, busy in the clinical room on the following day.

She was a fool to have fallen headlong in love with Mark, for instance. She might stir his senses but he didn't seem to like her very much. The dangerous flame apparently didn't need mutual liking for its spark.

In any case, he was going to marry the beautiful Louise Penistone. Gillian didn't wonder if he loved the girl. He was probably incapable of loving any woman for real, she thought heavily. He was too cold, too critical, too cautious to commit himself to that kind of caring. He meant to marry Louise because he was ambitious and hoped to gain eventual control of the clinic that her father had founded. Hurt and unhappy, Gillian decided that she despised him for it.

But it wasn't contempt that caused her heart to leap when he entered the room in obvious search of her. Knowing that he was about, she had taken refuge in a routine task, determined that she wouldn't be tempted into crossing his path in some way. She was afraid that the need to see him, if only at a distance, was becoming too obvious.

She paused in the act of taking sterile instruments from the autoclave and glanced at him, wary. The room was very light and spacious. It suddenly seemed much too small for two people. She could cope with the quickened beat of her heart and the turmoil of her senses when they only met briefly in a corridor or in the antiseptic surroundings of the theatre. Now, she feared that she might betray the upheaval of her emotions that he could cause without even trying.

'Can I help you?' she asked formally, carefully setting down the tray of instruments.

'You can give me your attention,' he said, dryly.

'What is it?' She refused to be distracted from a very automatic chore that she had carried out a thousand times. She preferred to be busy, the efficient nurse who never allowed personal feelings to get in the way of her work.

Mark went directly to the point. 'You're a very popular lady, aren't you? Much in demand. Robin McAllister. Steve. Others I don't know about, I expect. Whose turn is it tonight?'

Gillian stiffened at the hint of disapproval in his tone. She resented the arrogance that assumed he could question her behaviour. 'I shall probably stay in and wash my hair,' she said airily.

He reached to tuck a strand of the pale hair back under her cap. 'It doesn't seem to need it.' His fingers lingered lightly at the nape of her neck in that almost-caress that threatened to be her undoing.

With her heart pounding uncomfortably against her ribs, wishing he wasn't so unpredictable and so unsettling, Gillian moved from him in involuntary reaction to his touch. She began to arrange the newly sterilised instruments in their respective trays, her slender hands shaking slightly in the thin surgical gloves. The way he affected her was quite absurd, she told herself crossly.

Mark watched her, silent.

Gillian wondered what he wanted, why he had followed her into the room to talk to her. They seemed to have nothing to say to each other, after all.

'I've a message for you, Gillian,' he said at last.

She was surprised by the softening of his tone, by a warmth that seemed to take her name and turn it into an endearment.

But she continued to be busy. 'Oh . . . ?' She contrived to sound indifferent.

'From Henry. He wants to see you again.' His tone

was light, a smile lurking behind the words. 'He told me to ask you to dinner.'

Her heart shook for all the absurdity of the words. 'When?'

'Tonight.'

She couldn't look at him. She didn't trust the glow that she suddenly knew would be in his grey eyes, melting her foolish heart and the very bones in her body. She didn't understand and scarcely believed the invitation that had come out of the blue. 'Where?' Her voice was low, doubtful. But she was wavering in her resolution to fight his fascination for her with all her might.

'At his house.' Mark paused. 'I can give you the directions.' A smile flickered briefly.

'I don't know.' Gillian hesitated. 'I don't think I . . .'

'Please come,' he said quietly. 'Don't disappoint Henry. Or me.'

Gillian glanced at him then, uncertain. She was very tempted. There was something in his voice, in his eyes, that convinced her that he was not a man who was used to pleading for what he wanted. Either he took it or he walked away if it wasn't within easy reach, she felt. He was very proud. It couldn't be easy for a man like Mark Barlow to say *please* to a woman.

She was a fool but she desperately wanted that evening with the man she loved, so full of dangerous promise and offering no hope at all for the future. She was suddenly disinclined to question his motives. Perhaps he realised, just as she did, that it was their last chance to be in each other's arms. Tomorrow he would be engaged to Louise and she would have first claim on him. Gillian knew that she would never have any claim on him at all. But she loved him and she had to reach out for an hour of happiness, a glimpse of heaven, a brief and memorable magic.

She made up her mind abruptly. 'Tell Henry I'll be there,' she said in a rather flustered rush. She shut down the autoclave and hurried out of the clinical room like a very busy nurse without another moment to spare.

Later in the day, someone handed her a note, discreetly unsigned. It said simply:

Henry's expecting you for eight o'clock.
He lives at Croft House, Brookside.

For the rest of the day, Gillian puzzled over the invitation and wondered if she had been wise to accept it. What could Mark want from her except the one thing that she had always resolved never to surrender to any man until she married him? Why on earth was she rushing to burn her fingers at the flame of his too-blatant desire?

She didn't have to go, of course. Not turning up would probably cool his rather doubtful interest. He wouldn't care for being disappointed, thwarted.

Why was she going? Dressing carefully for the evening, Gillian asked herself the question—and couldn't find a convincing answer.

It would be madness to throw away her cherished virginity on a man who neither loved her nor wanted to marry her. She might regret it all her life. She didn't have the slightest doubt of the outcome if she spent the evening with a sensual man who stirred her own emotions so strongly. They would probably be alone in his house except for Henry—and she couldn't rely on the big black labrador to be an efficient chaperon, she thought dryly. He seemed to be actively encouraging matters if his master was to be believed!

She smiled at the whimsy. But it was out of character for someone like Mark and she wondered why he had resorted to it. He seemed so confident, so sure of where he was going and what he wanted in life. He could be direct to the point of rudeness. So it was strange that he had used the rapport which had leaped between his dog and herself that evening on the beach to persuade her into accepting an invitation.

But appealing to her sense of humour had worked, she thought dryly. Perhaps Mark had known that any other approach would result in failure. She hadn't felt kindly disposed towards him for days, she had been hurt and disappointed that he seemed able to pick her up and drop her as the fancy took him, convinced that it was only a sexually motivated fancy. But she had nothing against his dog . . .

Driving to his house on the other side of the town, Gillian felt that she was looking her best and wished that her foolish heart would quieten and allow her to concentrate on the traffic and the unfamiliar road.

The blue dinner dress with its diaphanous sleeves and low neckline flattered the slender lines of her figure and complemented the blonde of her hair and fair skin, the blue of her eyes. She had coiled her hair into a smooth chignon and taken pains with her make-up, and dabbed just a little of a very expensive French perfume on her pulses. Perhaps she couldn't compete with the beautiful Louise Peniston but she could hope to see a gleam of admiration and a glow of wanting in the eyes of the man who was waiting for her that evening.

She drove through impressive lych-gates in the modest little Mini and parked it beside the sleek and snobbish Mercedes that stood in the drive. The house was bigger than she had expected, obviously the home of a wealthy and successful man. For a moment she sat in the car and gazed at it, trying not to think that it might not be long before he was sharing it with a wife. She couldn't help wondering if it had been bought with marriage in mind. It was surely much too big for one man and his dog!

Gillian was nervous, slightly apprehensive. But she had it all under control as Mark came out of the house to greet her. She smiled at him coolly.

'I've a date with your dog,' she said, very bright.

He was cool, too. 'He's in the house. I knew you wouldn't want to be swept off your feet by an exuberant welcome.'

His glance took in the elegant dress, the high-heeled evening shoes, the sophisticated hair style and the careful make-up. She had never looked lovelier. But she was distant, keeping him carefully at arms' length. Mark was very determined that she should melt before the evening grew old.

Gillian wondered what she had expected as she accompanied him into the house after that light exchange which had said nothing of his feelings or her own. He wasn't a man to say what he didn't feel or mean. He didn't lavish compliments. A girl had to rely on the way he looked rather than what he said.

She was impressed by his home. It was expensively and tastefully furnished. He had some excellent prints and some exquisite porcelain, a vast array of stereo and video equipment, a well-stocked bar. She wondered if he played the magnificent grand piano that stood in a corner of the drawing-room.

It was very much a man's domain, lacking the little touches that a woman might have provided. But Gillian liked it. Mark's personality and strength of character and unexpected sensitivity had left a stamp on the room. Seeing him in the privacy of his home gave her a new insight into the man she loved. She suddenly realised how wrong it had been to be misled by his manner in the clinical surroundings of Greenvale or the antiseptic atmosphere of an operating theatre.

The black labrador was lying before the long window that opened on to a paved patio and a formal, well-kept garden. Nose on his paws, he was dozing in the last of the day's warmth. He looked up lazily, ears pricking very slightly, as they entered. After a few moments, he rose and padded across the room to Gillian and offered a polite paw, without enthusiasm. Gillian felt like an old and dear friend who could be relied on to understand when a dog just didn't feel like leaping up and barking a noisy welcome.

Used to dogs, she shook Henry's paw and pulled his ears and said all the right things. He grinned at her hugely and then went back to his rug and collapsed in a weary heap.

Gillian laughed.

Mark, busy with decanters, glanced at her with an appreciative twinkle in his eyes. 'He's worn out from hunting rabbits,' he explained. 'He came home filthy and exhausted after a day on the loose. He really isn't fit for decent company as a result. I shall have to banish him to the kitchen for the evening, I'm afraid.'

'So I won't have the pleasure of his company, after

all,' Gillian said, very light.

He smiled. 'You'll have the pleasure of *my* company.' He brought drinks and placed them on a low table.

'What more could any girl want?' she returned dryly.

He sat down on the deep-cushioned sofa beside her and leaned back with a sigh of content. 'I'm glad we've finally found common ground for agreement,' he drawled. 'I've had enough of fighting, Gillian.'

She was disturbed by his smile with its potent magnetism, tilting her heart. She didn't like the way her senses stirred at his nearness. She didn't trust herself not to turn and melt against him in swift, all-consuming wanting.

She reached for her drink. It was just as she liked it. 'Is it just us?' she asked, a little too casually. 'I mean—is anyone else coming?'

'It's just us.' Stretching out a hand for his whisky, his hand brushed her arm. He sensed the swift recoil from the light and quite accidental touch. He hoped it was nervousness and not an instinctive revulsion. He was hoping for great things from that evening with the girl he had wanted almost since the first moment of meeting.

'I can't believe that Henry has so few friends,' Gillian said lightly, hoping he hadn't noticed that involuntary reaction to his touch.

He smiled. 'My housekeeper can always manage one more for dinner but she likes rather more notice for a party.' He glanced at his watch. 'She's an excellent cook but we had to take a chance with the menu. I don't know your tastes in food.'

'Oh, anything! I haven't any fads or fancies after five years of the nurses' dining-room at Kit's,' she returned, smiling back at him. 'You can imagine what those meals were like! Plain and wholesome and lots of stodge to keep us going through the day and heaven help our figures!'

'It seems to have done wonders for yours,' he told her with an appreciative gleam in his grey eyes.

Enchanting warmth stole into her small and very pretty face, catching at his heart. Very few girls still knew how to blush, he thought dryly. Gillian did it beautifully. He touched his hand to the soft, flushed cheek in a rippling caress and saw that there was a hint of shy response in the guarded blue eyes. His heart moved unexpectedly.

He leaned to kiss her lips, very gently, tentatively. His fingers trailed from the lovely face to the slender throat and to the delicious swelling of the small breasts at the neck of her frock. There he paused, fingers warm against her soft and very tempting flesh, waiting for the smallest sign of encouragement.

Quickened by his kiss, his touch, Gillian was afraid to give too much too soon. He couldn't know that she was a virgin. He seemed to think she would be an easy conquest. There seemed to be an unnerving confidence rather than query in the way that he put his hand to her breast, the way he kissed her. She was torn between the longing to give, born of loving, and the natural reluctance to be taken too lightly by an unloving man.

His touch burned her body. The slow tide of desire was stealing through her veins. Her arms ached to hold him and her heart was struggling to speak its feelings.

She sat very still, tense, too shy to speak or make the smallest move towards yielding. She wanted to give him anything, everything. She wanted him to respect the value of the gift.

'Don't cheapen me, Mark,' she blurted. It wasn't at all

what she had meant to say and she knew instantly that it
had been a mistake.

The smile fled from his eyes and his hand fell from her
breast. He straightened, drank the whisky in his glass
and rose to his feet for a refill.

Gillian saw the nerve jumping in his jaw. She saw the
tightening of his mouth and the grimness of his expression. She saw the tension in his tall body. She swallowed
nervously.

'I meant . . . don't rush me,' she amended, low, a little
tremulous. She couldn't spell it out for him. Why didn't
he know what she was trying to say? With all his experience, he ought to know that she trembled on the
threshold of surrendering her most valuable asset, her
virginity.

He looked at her steadily. 'It has to be now. Or never,'
he said quietly. 'It's your last chance to make a fool of
me, Gillian.'

Her eyes widened at the bitterness of the words.
'That's never been my intention!' she said quickly,
defensively.

'I wonder.' Mark went to stand in front of the sofa,
looking down at her with a challenge in his eyes. 'Do you
know how many times you've slapped me down, knowing that I'd be back for more? Do you know how many
times I've said to hell with you and gone on wanting you
more than any woman I've ever known?' His voice
shook with sudden passion. 'Damn it, Gillian! I want
you. But I won't ask you again. Kiss me now and mean
it—or go right now!'

Shaken to the core of her being by the strength of
feeling that she had never suspected, Gillian rose and
went into his arms. She kissed him, lips warm and sweet

against his mouth, and felt the angry tension drain from him. She twined her fingers in the dark curls on the nape of his neck and allowed herself to yield to the tightening of his embrace.

'You never said . . .' she whispered, the secret places of her body licked with the fierce flame of response to the passion in him.

'I said it a dozen times. You didn't want to listen.' He could feel the heavy beat of her heart, her quickened breathing. The scent of her hair and her lovely body aroused all his sensuality. Now that he could be sure of the outcome, he could take his time and coax her gently towards the final surrender. He kissed her, light but full of promise, and let her go as the dinner gong sounded softly in the hall.

Gillian didn't know whether to be relieved or disappointed by the timely interruption. Things were happening too fast for her, she felt. The tide of desire was sweeping her into tempestuous and very dangerous waters. But without the impetus of his anger and her swift remorse, she might never have gone into his arms with a willingness that he probably assumed to be wanton.

Dinner was a very welcome breathing space, providing her with more insight into the man that she had loved before she really knew him. For he had arranged it to be intimate and much more romantic than she had expected of him.

There was candlelight and soft music and sparkling wine. There was a red rose, long-stemmed and thornless, the velvety petals still sparkling with evening dew from the garden, lying beside her plate in unmistakable compliment. There was Mark, so handsome in the formal black and white, so admiring and attentive and knowing just how to make a woman feel that she was something special in his life.

It might all be the prelude to seduction but Gillian was woman enough to thrill to it and she was rather flattered by the glow in his eyes, the warmth in his voice and the soft, subtle persuasion of a rare kind of lovemaking.

She relaxed and settled down to enjoy the evening and his company. He proved to be a very interesting and amusing host. Their mutual profession, with the common bond of a Kit's training and the recent association at Greenvale, combined with a shared sense of humour and a love of the ridiculous and similar tastes in music, art and books provided them with plenty to talk about and much more to like in each other than they had expected to find.

Later, Gillian made herself comfortable on the sofa, shoes kicked off, while he sat at the piano and played for her. All her favourites. Mozart, Brahms, a little Beethoven, some Strauss. He played well and with a sensitive touch, linking each piece of music with some improvisation of his own.

Gillian lay back against the cushions, listening raptly, admiring his good looks and the clever hands that seemed to be equally at home whether wielding the healing knife as a surgeon or playing beautiful music like a trained pianist or driving the sleek Mercedes like an expert. Or caressing a woman's slender body towards the ultimate ecstasy, she suddenly thought, with a catch of her breath as he glanced up and met her eyes.

He smiled, warm and enchanting and very endearing, tumbling her heart and her senses.

Gillian knew that she loved him very much. She stilled

the dismayed quiver of her heart because he would never be hers. She meant to be grateful for whatever the gods were kind enough to grant—even if it was only one night in the arms of the man she loved. She would give with all her heart for his delight, his satisfaction, she vowed.

She smiled at him with love, with tender longing, with unmistakable desire. On a sudden discord, he rose from the piano and moved towards her.

For a moment, he looked down at her, intently searching the lovely eyes that looked back at him so steadily. Then he bent to kiss her. Gillian drew him down to her, body arching. He pressed her close against the cushions and she knew the heavy throb of his body's leaping passion.

His kiss was urgent, demanding. His hands were busy with the long zip at the back of her dress and then he drew the thin material from her shoulders to bare the small, tilting breasts. He kissed each one, lips lingering on the enchanting buds of her nipples. Fire shot through her loins and she clung to him in sudden abandon, saying his name on a surge of longing.

He lifted her, carried her from the room against his heart. Effortlessly, he took the stairs, making nothing of her slender frame. Gillian's arms clung about his neck. She pressed her lips to his cheek, heart thudding, body swept with the flame of a desire that would not be denied.

She trembled on the threshold of a new and wonderful world that she would surely find in his embrace . . .

CHAPTER TWELVE

MARK undressed her with many kisses and infinite tenderness, every touch of his hands a homage to her beautiful body. Gillian was reassured by his gentleness, his patience. He made sensual love to her with slow, sweeping caresses. Wave after wave of delicious longing carried her closer to the ultimate surrender. She had never suspected the near-ecstasy that could vanquish all the natural hesitation of a girl who hovered between innocence and fulfilled womanhood.

Suddenly she panicked and pulled away from the urgency in his embrace. Controlling his disappointment, he kissed her and stroked the pale hair, soothed her gently.

She loved him for the self-control that wouldn't force her to give before she was ready. She loved him. She couldn't disappoint him—or herself.

She moved against him, kissed him with warm, sweet lips. His response was instant, demanding. He was trembling with the passion that insisted on satisfaction but which he was determined to school to ensure her fulfilment. He wanted this to be a memorable experience for them both. She was very lovely, very responsive and very dear to him.

At the last moment, she panicked again.

'For God's sake, Gillian!' The despairing reproach was wrenched from him. It took every ounce of his control to master the urge to take her by force.

'I'm sorry,' she said swiftly, penitent. 'I'm not teasing. Truly I'm not. I'm just scared . . .'

He swept the hair from her face and searched the shy eyes, puzzled. 'Tell me why.'

She laid her hand on his cheek in a caress. 'It's the first time,' she said simply.

He was stilled, astonished, profoundly thankful that her response to his lovemaking, so sweet and so sensuous, had been born of instinct rather than experience.

Then he kissed her, with love. 'Then I'm honoured,' he said softly.

Gillian was glad that she had told him. He couldn't be anything but gentle, patient, very tender. But there was a hint of reverence in his taking of her that filled her with new and deeper love for him.

It was magic.

It was heaven there and then.

But only because she loved him with all her heart.

'I love you,' she said on a murmuring sigh as he lay on her breast, spent and content. She stroked the crisp dark curls, the strong neck, the bare shoulder with its rippling muscles.

She sensed his smile, lazy and accepting.

'Lovely Gillian,' he said, his arm tightening about her. He didn't believe the words she had spoken in the golden aftermath of their lovemaking. Women often spoke of loving at such times. It seemed to ease a foolish sense of guilt that a man neither experienced nor really understood.

He was very near to loving her, he knew . . . nearer than he had been in all his life to a final commitment to a woman. But he had to be very sure. That kind of loving could never be easy for a man of his proud and independent spirit. When he loved, it would be lasting. It would need a very special woman to content him for the rest of his life, he felt.

Just now, he believed that Gillian might be that woman. But until he was really sure he wouldn't say. He didn't know how he hurt her sensitive feelings with that non-commital reply.

Gillian had given all she could, heart and soul and body. All she asked of him was a kindly lie, she thought sadly, a fleeting reassurance that she mattered to him.

Later, she would be glad and grateful that he couldn't be anything but honest, she knew.

Just now, she wished that he could pretend to love . . .

They drowsed in each other's arms, lovers reluctant to part. Gillian didn't want the night to end. For a few hours, he was hers—and she might never have anything more to remember. At least she had this memory of tender and very precious delight and she knew she would cherish it for ever.

One day, there might be another love in her life. But there would never be anyone quite like Mark. He would always have a very special place in her heart and mind. He was her first love. She was glad that he was her first lover. It proved that she had been right to hold on to her virginity until this moment and this man came together.

They slept and made love again in the early morning, without tension or haste. He knew just how to please and delight her, Gillian thought, heart welling as they clung to each other in mutual and magical wanting.

She fell more deeply into love with each kiss, every touch of that languorous lovemaking—and, loving him, she refused to remember that he would soon belong to someone else. Loving him, she clung desperately to the dream that he loved her . . .

Mark rolled over to look at his watch. 'It is Saturday, isn't it?' No clinic, no appointments, no need to end the idyll too soon.

She leaned across him. 'No, it's ten to six,' she said lightly.

He laughed. 'The girl who came to dinner and stayed for breakfast,' he teased softly.

Colour prettied her small face in the way that he loved. He kissed her.

'I don't regret it,' Gillian said quietly.

'Do you think that *I* do?' He thrust his hands through the silken cloud of her hair to cradle her small head. 'I've only one regret,' he said tensely. 'We wasted too much time, Gillian.'

She was suddenly emotional, tears in her eyes. She felt that he was reminding her that the dream was about to end. It was Saturday. It was the day of Hugh Penistone's birthday and the dinner party that would also celebrate Mark's decision to marry the man's daughter, made long before she had come to Greenvale. Time had run out. His life, if not his love, would be committed to the lovely Louise in future. She felt he would be loyal. He might be a sensual man but he was also a sensitive one and she knew he wouldn't lie in her arms once he had promised to marry someone else.

Gillian was too proud to let him see those tears or realise the terrible heaviness of her heart. She had known from the beginning that there was no future in loving him. Heaven knew that he hadn't encouraged her to love him or given her the slightest reason to suppose that he would ever love her. Even the night in his arms had passed without one word of love from him, she thought bleakly.

'You shouldn't have been such a pig,' she said lightly. 'I might have liked you sooner.' She rubbed her cheek against his bare shoulder.

He smiled wryly. 'I couldn't get close to you for prickles,' he reminded her, very dry. He drew her down into his arms and she nestled against him, storing up every memorable moment for comfort in the days when she would miss him and mourn him with all her heart.

But she didn't mean to spoil the lovely present with bleak thoughts of the future. She would simply make the most of the moments that she had left to her.

They lay in the wide bed, talking, kissing, teasing each other like long-time lovers. Being together was so right, Mark felt, content and comfortable in her company. He had never felt quite so relaxed with any woman. She was all that any man could want, he felt—even a man as self-sufficient as he had always been. He was tempted to tell her that he would want her for the rest of his life.

But there was plenty of time, he decided.

He knew that Hugh Penistone hoped that he would marry Louise. He knew that Louise thought she had brought him to the point of proposing. He knew the rumours that were flying about the town thanks to Louise and her friends.

He had toyed with the idea. Louise was beautiful, sophisticated, clever and confident. She had seemed a suitable wife for a man in his position. He realised that she was spoiled and selfish and superficial but most of the women he knew were much the same.

It had taken someone like Gillian, with her refreshing honesty and proud spirit and innate warmth of heart to show him that he needed much more from a woman than Louise could ever give him. For some days, he had known that he wouldn't ask her to marry him. He had been trying to let her down gently. They had known each other for a long time and he was fond of her. But he would have to be more blunt with her that evening. He didn't think she would be too hurt or too disappointed. She didn't love him any more than he loved her.

He regretted that he wouldn't be able to see Gillian that evening. But there would be plenty of other evenings now that he had broken through the barrier of her mistrust and won the liking that was so important to him. There would be all the time in the world to clarify the way they really felt about each other and discover if it was destined to lead to marriage, he thought confidently.

Meanwhile Gillian fretted because they seemed to talk of everything but the Penistones. She couldn't mention father or daughter or the pending dinner party. Mark had never discussed his relationship with Louise or his plans where the girl was concerned and Gillian was much too proud to ask if he meant to marry her. But so many rumours couldn't have sprung out of thin air, she thought heavily. Besides, it seemed that rumour had turned into concrete fact during the last few days. Everyone was expecting an engagement to be announced that weekend . . .

Reluctantly, they got up at last and took it in turns to shower. Dressed in jeans and a bright orange shirt, Mark went down to cook breakfast for them both. His elderly housekeeper didn't live in and he was used to looking after himself in her absence.

Released from his confinement in the kitchen, Henry

went wild in the garden, barking at the birds and chasing imaginary cats as if he was a puppy instead of a respectable eight-year old. Mark decided to bath him after his adventures with the rabbits, declaring that he smelled to high heaven. Gillian helped, her slight figure enveloped in one of Mark's bathrobes. Her elegant dinner frock was scarcely suitable for struggling with a wet and exuberant and very solid labrador.

She rolled in the grass with him, giggling as if she were an eight-year old instead of a highly-trained and very efficient theatre nurse. Watching, Mark felt his heart turn over in his breast, proving that it wasn't a medical impossibility. She was so lovely, so appealing, so very natural—and so unlike any other girl that he had ever known.

Whatever happened, he mustn't lose her!

He drew her up and into his arms and held her close, cheek pressed to the rumpled mass of her pale hair. 'Oh, Gillian . . .' he said achingly, moved almost beyond expression by a new and quite overwhelming dependence on her for his happiness.

She stood in his arms, thankful, heart soaring. Surely there was all the loving and longing that any woman could want in the way he held her, the way he looked. What words did she need?

No words were said, in fact. But she felt there had been a promise in his parting kiss when she finally drove away in her Mini, much later that morning, on her way home.

Somehow the flat didn't feel like home any more. She let herself in, carrying the daily pinta, scooped some letters from the floor and went into the kitchen. She filled the kettle and switched it on for coffee and then she went to change. Her frock had been so right for the previous evening. In the bright light of day, it was incongruous.

Gillian looked at herself in the long mirror and wondered why she didn't look different. She felt different! She felt alive and glowing and touched by enchantment. She felt loved and she didn't care if the whole world declared that Mark meant to marry Louise Penistone. Perhaps it had been in his mind. But she just didn't believe that he could do it. Not now. Not when they were so right for each other!

The euphoria didn't last. Her confidence began to ebb as the memory of the magic became overshadowed by the realisation that he had said not one real word of love to her for all that night in his arms. Had she really thought that of all the women who must have enjoyed his sensual lovemaking *she* was special? Had she really imagined that her love for him was the key to lasting happiness?

They had parted with no arrangement to meet again. Obviously she would see him at Greenvale, but those impersonal surroundings could stifle anyone's feelings and they would need to be discreet or set the grapevine buzzing.

Mark hadn't mentioned the Penistones. She knew, because everyone else did, that he was one of the main guests at Hugh Penistone's birthday dinner. She didn't want to think of him spending the evening with the beautiful Louise by his side, perhaps wondering why he shouldn't carry out his original intention of asking her to marry him.

Why should he remember Gillian in his arms or feel that their lovemaking should affect his long-standing decision to acquire an eminently suitable wife for a successful surgeon? It seemed only too likely that men like Mark took girls like herself to bed and then forgot them. They married the Louise Penistones of their world!

Her heart grew heavier as she busied herself with necesssary chores about the flat. She decided to go shopping that afternoon—and almost the first person she saw was Mark.

His height and striking good looks made him an unmistakable figure among the crowd of shoppers in the High Street. Instinctively she quickened her steps to reach him as he paused outside the shop he had just left. She desperately needed to see and speak to him if only for a moment. She needed the reassurance of a smile, a word, a loving glance.

She didn't know if he had seen her. But he suddenly turned and began to walk quickly in the opposite direction. Hesitating, Gillian realised that he had come out of a jewellers, the most exclusive and expensive in the town. He had put something away in his pocket as he stood outside the shop. A small square box, perhaps. Maybe one that contained a ring. The engagement ring he had chosen for Louise?

Gillian's heart plummeted like a stone.

What else?

Everyone knew of the engagement. She could almost visualise the enormous diamond solitaire on its velvet cushion that he must have bought for the girl he meant to marry.

No wonder he hadn't wanted to speak to her, Gillian thought bleakly. He must have seen her hurrying along the pavement towards him. He had been looking at her!

He was going through with it. The gift of her love, of herself, meant absolutely nothing to him. He meant to marry Louise because he was a proud, ambitious, cold-hearted man who was quite incapable of loving any woman.

Gillian turned and made her way back to the flat, seeing nothing and no one, buying none of the essential items that had taken her out that afternoon. She was struggling with the most dreadful pain that radiated from the region of her heart and turned her limbs to lead and her blood to ice-water.

Of course Mark didn't love her. She had always known that there was no future in loving him. She had walked into his arms with her eyes wide open and it was much too late for regrets. He had taken what she offered just as any man would.

At least he had spared her the lie that he loved her, she thought bleakly. She couldn't have coped with that amount of hurt.

She shrivelled at the memory of her own declaration of love. He had been drowsy, drifting into sleep— Perhaps he hadn't heard! But his arm had tightened about her and she had known that he smiled and he had murmured her name in lazy response. Of course he had heard.

She could only hope that he hadn't believed her. People did say such things at such times, she knew. She couldn't bear it if Mark knew how she felt about him and just didn't care! She couldn't bear it if he dismissed her love with that mocking contempt he seemed to show for all the women who paraded their desire for him! She wouldn't let him trample her heart beneath his uncaring feet. She must find a way to convince him that she didn't love him at all!

There was Robin, she thought thankfully. Dear, loyal, loving Robin who had come back into her life just when she needed him most.

Louise Penistone's engagement didn't have to be the only one that was announced that weekend, she thought with a desperation born of pride, dialling Robin's telephone number and knowing that he wouldn't let her down . . .

Gillian was numb.

She talked and smiled and laughed and danced in Robin's arms and gave a convincing performance of happiness at the Country Club that evening. It was all for Robin's sake. He didn't deserve the hurt and humiliation of knowing that he was being used to protect her pride.

There was a buzz of speculation about the party at the Penistones. It was a private party with very few guests. No one seemed to doubt the outcome. Gillian tried not to listen to the gossip and had nothing to say about Mark Barlow's plans. She did work with him but she scarcely knew him, she insisted brightly. She was a newcomer to the clinic. She didn't know Louise Penistone except by sight. She was very beautiful and very smart. Everyone seemed to think that the surgeon and Hugh Penistone's daughter were well suited, she agreed—and drew Robin out to the dance floor to escape any more talk about the couple before she betrayed the dead thing in her breast that she called her heart.

As they danced, Robin drew her close with proud and tender possessiveness. She was so pretty and so sweet, so popular among his friends with her easy friendliness and bright humour and love of life.

He loved her very much. But it was a long time since they had been close enough for him to know her every mood. In three years, Gillian had matured and grown away from him and it would take a little time to regain their former intimacy and understanding. So he wasn't sensitive to the misery behind the sparkle in her lovely eyes.

She seemed happy and relaxed, glad to be with him, and Robin didn't look beyond the obvious. He was too relieved. She had seemed to be keeping him at a slight distance. She had been insisting on her independence. She had encouraged Steve Palmer's interest too much for his peace of mind.

Now, she was affectionate and dependent and encouraging, referring lightly to the future as though there wasn't the slightest doubt that they would spend it together. Robin decided that she had just needed a few days to sort out her feelings after the surprise of meeting him again.

Gillian smiled at him. Dear Robin. He was so nice, so reliable. He was familiar and kind and reassuring and she knew exactly where she stood with him. Married to him, a girl would be safe. He might not be exciting but he was dependable and he would never hurt or humiliate her by taking everything and giving nothing.

The lurking pain began to creep up on her again. She forced it back. As long as she didn't feel anything she could contemplate marrying a man she would never, never love. She wouldn't think about Mark and the might have been. She would concentrate on Robin and the will-be!

Her hand tightened on his shoulder. 'I'm so glad we found each other again,' she said warmly. 'I missed you a lot when you left Kit's. I'm afraid I must have hurt you very much,' she added with new understanding and a great deal of compassion.

Robin was surprised by the sudden reference to the past and touched by the remorse in her soft voice. He brushed his lips against her hair. 'That's all forgotten, darling,' he assured her tenderly. 'We were lucky to be given the chance of a new beginning.'

'I think I can promise you a happy ending,' Gillian said. 'If you still want me . . .'

Taken by surprise, he missed a step, a rare event for such an expert dancer. 'Do you mean it? *Will* you marry me?' he asked eagerly.

She nodded. Words were too difficult.

He caught her close and kissed her in the middle of the crowded dance floor, a rare event for such an undemonstrative man. 'Soon?'

'Whenever you like,' Gillian said bleakly.

He was too delighted to realise the sadness in her eyes or the despair in her voice. He was over the moon, exultant, excited, making plans. She didn't have to say very much at all for the rest of the evening for Robin was voluble with happiness and relief, and confidence in the future.

He didn't question if she loved him, Gillian thought, relieved. To someone as uncomplicated as Robin there couldn't be any other reason why she would want to marry him. He wouldn't understand that a girl could be driven by pride and pain and a hopeless passion for one man to seek refuge in the arms of another who had loved her so long and so loyally.

An evening with his friends turned into a celebration and it was late before he took her home. Gillian wished she could say goodnight and send him away with a chaste kiss. But a man who was expecting to marry the woman he loved in the near future also expected more than a kiss to seal the bargain, she told herself heavily.

He had been very patient. Somehow she must let him into her arms and try to respond to his ardour. It wouldn't be possible to say no to him once she was his wife.

If she had only said no to Mark then she might not be so reluctant to lie in Robin's loving arms, she thought with the beginning of pain that the magic had fled so soon.

Comparisons were odious, she told herself fiercely, unmoved by Robin's warm lips on her own, his tentative caress of her breast, trying not to shrink from him. Her body was cold and heavy and unwilling.

He kissed her gently and without fire. There wasn't the urgency in his embrace that she had expected and dreaded. She realised that he was keeping a tight rein on his feelings. She was surprised and relieved when he released her with a last kiss.

'Darling, I'd better go,' he said wryly. 'I want you too much . . .' She felt obliged to tell him that he didn't have to go. He smiled and shook his head. 'It's like you to be generous. You're very sweet,' he told her warmly. 'But I've waited so long for you that a few more weeks won't be any hardship. Besides, I'm old-fashioned enough to want a virgin for my bride.'

Gillian knew she should disillusion him then and there. She simply couldn't. She kissed him and let him go, happy in his ignorance.

She hadn't known that it was so easy to commit herself to an unwanted future. Now, she wouldn't have that year at Greenvale, after all. Robin wanted an early wedding and she knew his views on working wives. Mark would have to find someone else to take over as his theatre nurse, she thought with a wrench of disappointment. But she knew she couldn't have taken the job, anyway.

Even a Kit's nurse could find it impossible to separate the personal from the professional when she found herself deeply in love with a surgeon . . .

CHAPTER THIRTEEN

GILLIAN didn't sleep at all.

Her thoughts wound themselves ceaselessly around a trio of doctors. A surgeon, a GP and an anaesthetist. Hopelessly in love with the first, foolishly engaged to the second, she almost found herself wishing that she had settled for the unalarming and undemanding third!

She was tormented by doubts and anxieties and regrets. She wandered aimlessly about the lonely, echoing flat. She sat with her head in her hands. She went to bed and got up again. The night seemed endless, an eternity of pain and despair. She cried for Mark, for Robin, for herself.

Mark didn't deserve to be loved so much. Robin didn't deserve to be loved so little. And did she deserve to be so wretched and so miserable when all she had done was fall in love with the wrong man?

Doubting that Mark was alone and lonely that night, wondering if he thought of her at all she remembered the magic that they had too briefly known. Gillian clenched her hands so fiercely that the nails dug tiny crescents into her palms. She didn't notice the hurt. She hurt all over.

Later, she might be able to re-discover her pride and determine never to cry again for Mark or to allow him to break her heart. Just now, she was a crumpled heap of misery.

She was huddled on the shabby sofa in her dressing-gown, clasping a steaming mug of coffee in both hands for comfort, when the telephone rang just after nine o'clock the next morning.

She reached for the receiver without enthusiasm, expecting Robin.

It was Steve.

'Hallo, love. I'm just off to the golf course but I wondered if you'd heard the news?'

'What news?' She was too tired to care.

'About Mark?' He was gently probing.

'Oh, that! I know!' she said quickly, defensive, not wanting to talk about Mark or anything that affected him. She hadn't thought that Steve could be so insensitive, she thought bitterly. Or was he just trying to be kind, to forewarn her, to protect her from betraying dismay when someone else informed her that the long-expected engagement was finally fact? She suspected that Steve had always known that her stubborn dislike of Mark was a defence.

'You know?'

She was too cold and too dispirited to notice the surprise. 'Yes.'

'What's your reaction?' he asked with the genuine interest of a caring friend.

'Complete indifference,' she said on a surge of pride. 'I don't know him well enough to care one way or the other. Frankly, I'm just not interested!' Wishing him an enjoyable game of golf, she rang off before the conversation could develop any further—and it was some minutes before she realised that she hadn't told him of her own wedding plans.

Well, it wasn't the kind of news to break over the telephone to a man who was fond of her and showed it. It wouldn't break his heart, she knew—and thanked heaven for it. He was a good friend who really cared that she should be happy. All she had to do was to convince him that marrying Robin would make her happy. The red-haired anaesthetist could be unexpectedly perceptive and much too shrewd for comfort at times.

Half an hour later, the telephone shrilled its loud summons throughout the flat once more. It really had to be Robin this time, Gillian decided.

She put down her hair-brush and reluctantly rose from the dressing-table and went into the living-room to answer. With very little heart for the task, she had been trying to repair some of the ravages of an obviously sleepless night. She was pale and there were violet smudges beneath her eyes, even her hair had lost its usual shining bounce.

She picked up the receiver and gave the number, doing her best to sound bright and cheerful for Robin.

'Gillian?'

Her heart froze. Without conscious thought, she slammed down the receiver. How dared he! How could he!

Moments later, the telephone rang again. Gillian stared at it, tense, torn between the need to talk to him and a natural contempt for a man who promised to marry one woman and pursued another in almost the same breath.

She picked up the receiver, trembling, her heart thudding.

'Gillian? It's Mark.'

'What do you want?' she asked stonily.

'To talk to you, of course.' There was a caress in his warm voice. 'Steve gave me your number.'

'I can't talk . . . not just now,' she said stiffly, choked with sudden tears.

'Aren't you alone?' he asked lightly.

'Of course I'm alone!' she said fiercely, bridling, angry pride conquering the rush of foolish, futile tears.

'Did I get you out of bed?'

'No.'

'It sounds as if all the prickles are back,' he told her, warm, teasing.

'What did you expect?'

There was a moment's silence at his end. Then he said quietly: 'Gillian, what is it? You seem angry. I hope you aren't hating me all over again?'

'Well, I am!' she said, proud, and hung up before he could weaken her resolution with the seeming concern in his tone.

Then she took the telephone off the hook.

Perhaps he wouldn't ring her again. Perhaps he would shrug those broad shoulders and accept that it was over and even be relieved that she didn't mean to make any embarrassing or unwelcome demands on him. But Gillian wasn't going to risk it. She couldn't bear to talk to him while her heart was so full. She wanted him so much that it might be too easy to forgive him and do anything he asked.

She was thankful that she wasn't on duty at weekends. At least she wouldn't run the risk of seeing him at the clinic that day and she wouldn't have to endure the excited chatter of patients and staff about his engagement to Louise Penistone.

By the time she did meet Mark, she meant to have her heart firmly under control and he wouldn't be able to melt her with the coaxing warmth in his deep voice or the smile in his eyes, she determined proudly.

It was a beautiful day. It didn't seem right that the sun

could shine so brilliantly from a cloudless blue sky when her heart was so heavy. Grey skies and drenching rain would have been much more appropriate, she felt.

She didn't want to stay in the flat. She was much too restless, too wretched. She didn't want to see Robin who would certainly call at the flat when he couldn't reach her by telephone. He would have all the days of her life. She needed this one for herself.

She took the Mini and drove to the quiet stretch of coast where she had met Mark on that wet and wind-swept evening and begun to like him. She needed to be alone and she needed to think about Mark and come to terms with the bleakness of her life without him, and she needed the nearness of the sea with its soothing, calming influence.

She walked for a while, slowly, scuffing her feet in the wet sand. There weren't too many people about and no one took any notice of the slight figure in jeans and pale blue cotton blouse, hair tied loosely at her neck with a pale blue ribbon.

She paused to sit in the small wooden shelter, hugging her arms across her troubled breast, watching the waves surging against the shore as the tide came in and listening to the song of the sea and the whisper of the wind. The wind and the waves seemed to have only one sound that day . . . the persistent throb of a man's name.

Foolishly, she slipped into a world of dreaming. A world where Mark held her in strong arms and kept her safe and content. A world where Robin and Louise had no place at all. A world of loving between a man and a woman who had been meant to meet and come together. For what else but destiny could have brought her all the way from Kit's to a private clinic in the heart of Sussex so that she could fall deeply, irrevocably and quite hopelessly in love?

Destiny could be very cruel, she thought wistfully. Why couldn't she have loved Robin, so dear and familiar and deserving? Or Steve with his admiration and affection and warm, friendly support?

She had disliked and despised Mark when she first met him. She hadn't encouraged his interest or wanted to be involved with him. She had resisted the tug of his physical magnetism and powerful personality for as long as she could. Why did she feel that he was all her happiness, the only man she would ever love and need, when he was the one man that she had been a fool to love?

A shadow fell across her as a tall figure blocked out the sun. Gillian glanced up, startled. Henry bounded forward and laid his head confidently on her knee and gave a light, friendly bark. Mark smiled down at her, just as confident of a welcome.

Her face blanched with the shock of seeing him and her heart missed a beat. She thrust the dog away from her involuntarily and wished she could do the same to his master.

'I said I didn't want to see you!' she said bitterly.

Mark crouched on his haunches to look into the small, stormy face and took the cold hands into his own. 'What's it all about, Gillian?' His tone was gentle. His heart was very fearful.

She wouldn't meet his eyes. 'How did you know I'd be here?' She resented his intrusion into her privacy. She wouldn't melt at his touch, his obvious concern.

'You weren't at the flat. You seemed to be cross and I thought you might be walking it off and I remembered that you came here before when you had something on your mind. It was worth a try. Then I saw your Mini.' A smile flickered in the grey eyes. 'I'm learning to love that car,' he told her lightly.

He couldn't make her smile. She looked past him to the rejected labrador who was consoling himself by digging a deep hole in the sand in search of treasure.

She tried to free her hands from his firm, determined clasp. 'I wish you'd go away and leave me alone,' she said fiercely. 'I don't want anything more to do with you—ever!'

His eyes narrowed at the hot words and the cold anger that prompted them. He searched the defiant blue eyes, dismayed.

He was hurt and baffled by her attitude. He could understand her natural reaction to the loss of her virginity to a man she scarcely knew. He had swept her off her feet and into bed with the urgency of his passion. Regret, some doubt, even anxiety were understandable and could be soothed away with the right words. He hadn't expected this anger, this loathing, this hurtful rejection.

'You're sorry that you slept with me? Is that it? Do you know how bad that makes me feel?' he asked quietly, with pain.

He released her hands and straightened and turned to stare at the gently rippling sea, proud and controlled. With a throbbing heart, Gillian looked at the handsome, suddenly stern face and the set of his broad shoulders, the clench of his hands. She almost believed that she had hurt him.

She hardened her heart. 'You used me,' she said stiffly. 'Do you know how bad that makes *me* feel?'

He turned, incredulous, instantly contrite. 'Then I've

been very clumsy and you've every right to be angry!' he said swiftly.

Gillian was moved almost to tears by the genuine contrition and concern. There were depths to this man that she had never suspected when she first knew him. He had seemed so proud, so arrogant, so hard and uncaring. But he was sensitive and kind, capable of tenderness and humility and an endearing humour. He was warm and strong and gentle. He was everything that she had ever hoped for in a man. He was the only man that she would ever love.

And she couldn't say so.

So she said nothing.

Mark was beginning to feel desperate. He had tried to assure her that it wasn't just a casual and meaningless sexual encounter. He had wanted her to know that he regarded that night with each other as a commitment. He had never been so ready to love any woman. He knew that he didn't want to lose her now. He couldn't let her walk out of his life.

He stretched out his hand to touch her pale cheek in a tentative caress. 'I bought something for you yesterday,' he said quietly. 'I meant to give it to you today. Now I wonder if I should wait for tomorrow. If there's going to be any tomorrow for us, Gillian?' He was pleading, pride forgotten.

Her heart swelled. How could he suppose that they had any future when the present was so complicated by his engagement to Louise and her own promise to marry Robin? She didn't even know what he was asking of her. To be his mistress until he tired of her? To be content with the little he gave while the whole of his life was promised to another woman?

Loving him, needed him, Gillian still couldn't settle for an empty, meaningless relationship. She shook her head. 'No. It's over, Mark. I mean it.'

Her coldness smote him to the heart. But he couldn't accept the words. She was much too important to him.

'This isn't the Gillian that Henry knows and loves,' he said, striving for lightness, for his happiness, striving to warm the heart which had turned against him.

'No! It's the Gillian that's going to marry Robin McAllister!' she flared suddenly, furiously, feeling that he was entirely to blame for the foolish impulse that had urged her into that engagement.

His eyes were suddenly frightening chips of granite in a very stern face. 'When did that happen?' he demanded.

'Does it matter?' Her chin shot up at the autocratic tone. It was none of his business, she thought bitterly. Had she demanded to know any of the details about his engagement to Louise Penistone? He hadn't even had the decency to tell her about it himself!

'It matters a hell of a lot! Tell me!'

He was so forceful, his eyes blazing with such icy anger, that Gillian heard herself saying lamely: 'Last night . . . he asked me last night.'

'And you said yes? Just like that? I don't believe it,' he said bluntly.

She had seemed to be so happy in his arms such a short time before. She had seemed to know as surely as he did that it was a beginning and he just couldn't believe that she had been so ready to end it at a word from McAllister. She had said *I love you* and while he had doubted if she meant the warm, impulsive words, he had hoped that time would turn them into welcome reality.

She looked at him. 'Well, it's true. I'm engaged to Robin. It should have happened a long time ago,' she said defiantly.

'You're a fool, Gillian. You don't love the man,' he said impatiently, dismissively.

Gillian bridled. He had forfeited all right to know whether she loved or didn't love! 'I'm the best judge of the way I feel about Robin, don't you think?' she returned coldly, with spirit.

'No, I don't,' he said brusquely, not mincing matters. 'But I can't stop you if you're set on marrying the poor devil. It's your life.' He spun on his heel and walked away from her, whistling to Henry. He was furious, shattered. He was very sure that it would be a long time before he came so near to loving again. Damn her! She had made a fool of him, after all!

Gillian looked after his tall, uncompromising figure, sick and shaken. It had only needed the right words and she would have sacrificed all Robin's loving and caring for the little happiness she might find with Mark, however fleeting. But he hadn't said anything. He was indifferent. He didn't care if she married Robin or any other man. He just didn't care . . .

Suddenly Mark turned and came back, taking a small, square box from his jacket pocket. 'You might as well have this, anyway,' he said harshly. 'It's only a trinket. Call it a memento. Do what you like with it. It isn't any good to me now.' He tossed the box into her lap Then he was gone, striding fast and furious along the beach.

Gillian didn't want anything from him but the one thing that he would probably never give to any woman. His real and lasting love. She couldn't imagine what he had bought for her. She didn't really care, she told herself proudly.

But she was much too feminine to resist the curious urge to find out. She opened the box and discovered a gold ring, two sculptured hearts entwined on a slender band. Her own heart shook as she stared at it in disbelief.

She ran after him impulsively. 'Mark! Wait, Mark!'

Having reluctantly left his fascinating hole in the sand at last, Henry ran with her, leaping, barking, loving the game.

Mark didn't slacken his stride.

Gillian caught up with him, tugged at his arm. He halted and looked down at her. At the look in his eyes, her heart faltered.

She held out the ring box. 'I can't take this, Mark. It's beautiful but I don't want it,' she said unhappily.

He shrugged. 'Then throw it in the sea.'

'I can't do that!'

'Why not? It doesn't seem to mean anything to you,' he challenged.

'It might have meant everything,' she said, low, tremulous. Tears brimmed suddenly in her eyes. She looked up at him, no longer proud. Loving him, she needed to know what had prompted the gift. 'Why did you buy it, Mark?'

He hesitated. Then he smiled and brushed a tear from her thick lashes with a tender finger and saw that she quivered at his touch. His heart contracted. 'You'd given me so much,' he said quietly and with truth. 'I wanted to give you something to show that you're special in my life. It's the way I feel.'

'How can I be special? You're going to marry Louise,' Gillian said bleakly.

Mark suddenly understood and wondered why he hadn't realised that the absurd gossip about himself and Louise must have reached her ears and might even have hurt her. It might certainly be the reason why she had snubbed him so persistently when all his instincts had insisted that they were meant for each other.

He put his arms about her slight and very feminine body. 'No, I'm not,' he said gently.

She was suddenly very tense, eyes enormous in the small face. 'You aren't?'

'Any more than you're going to marry McAllister,' he said firmly. 'Henry would never allow it.'

The black labrador, sitting quietly on a clump of rock and waiting patiently until his master should be ready to walk on, heard the mention of his name and uttered an affirmative bark.

Gillian smiled through sparkling tears of happiness. 'Does Henry have the last word on everything?' she demanded, her heart lifting at the promise in his eyes and voice, feeling herself surrounded by the warmth of his love. Her despair and heartache had been short-lived, after all. But it had taught her to value even more the precious gift of their mutual and lasting need.

'Absolutely. He runs my life for me. He doesn't like Louise but that's only one of the reasons why I didn't ask her to marry me as everyone expected. Including you, it seems,' he added, very light, giving her a little shake of tender reproach. 'You might have trusted me more!'

'You never said a word to me,' she reminded him, reproachful in her turn. 'How could I know what you meant to do?'

'I didn't think it was necessary. Louise didn't seem to have anything to do with you and me.' He stroked a strand of soft hair from her small face with a great deal of tenderness in his touch. 'You mean that I didn't say that I loved you,' he said quietly. His arms tightened about her and he pressed his lips to her hair. 'I'm saying it now, Gillian. I love you very much. I've waited a long time for you and I need you in my life.' He smiled down at her, suddenly warm. 'Come live with Henry and me and be our love . . .' His voice was low, persuasive. His grey eyes were filled with the smile that had captured her heart long before she was ready to admit it.

He kissed her hair, her cheek. She turned her face to him and their lips met in a kiss that sealed the promise for the future and stirred them both to new heights of loving and wanting.

So much more than the bright and dangerous flame of sexual desire leaped between them as they kissed on that sun-soaked beach with the seagulls soaring and swooping overhead and the tide turning on the shore.

Out of that trio of doctors, Gillian had followed her destiny and chosen the one man who was capable of loving her with all the passion and the power and the glory of a deep and lasting emotion to match that in her own heart . . .

Doctor Nurse Romances

Amongst the intense emotional pressures of modern medical life, doctors and nurses often find romance. Read about their lives and loves in the other three Doctor Nurse titles available this month.

AUSTRIAN INTERLUDE
by Lee Stafford

Melody Cameron finds a happiness she had never dreamed of when she takes on a private nursing assignment near the beautiful Austrian city of Salzburg. But can her feelings for Dr Dieter von Rheinhof bring her anything more than heartache?

SECOND CHANCE AT LOVE
by Zara Holman

Sister Hana Dean had left her post at a London teaching hospital because of an unhappy love affair. So when she clashes with surgeon Jake Carlyon at the Bridgestead Cottage Hospital can her self-respect allow him to drive her back?

CASSANDRA BY CHANCE
by Betty Neels

Benedict van Manfeld, a brilliant surgeon whose sight had been severely damaged in an accident, has some excuse for his ill-temper. But is that the only reason Nurse Cassandra Darling continues to put up with his ranting and raging?

Mills & Boon
the rose of romance